RELEASE THE BELGIUM

By

Robert E. Petras Sr

1

ISBN: 978-1-961028-19-7

Dedicated to Bella Petras and Bianca Petras, my two granddaughters, coming of age. Don't do as I did. Do as you do.

Contents

ABOUT THE AUTHOR 5

FOREWORD 7

RELEASE THE BELGIUM 9

FAST-TWITCH JEANS 14

HALFTIME 20

THE CALLING 24

SOUL TWINKERS 33

STEALING HOME 40

TACK-TICS 49

STANDOUTS 54

MONKEY IN THE MIDDLE 61

THE BELGIUM 65

MEDITATIONS FROM A TREEHOUSE 71

JAIL 77

HOME 82

CASTS 88

RELEASE 94

OLLIE OLLIE IN COME FREE 98

A T-TOWN CITY SIX PACK 103

THE PHANTOM FARTER 104

CROWIN' 111

GEMMING THE GYM CITY 118

MUSCLE BEACH 124

THE ABDOMINAL SNOWMAN OF MOUNT KNEE BOW 130

TALES OF CAMP CRUMB 137

ABOUT THE AUTHOR

Robert Petras Sr. is a poet, author, blogger, historian, nutritionist and certified personal trainer from the little eastern Ohio town of Toronto.

He developed an early interest in journalism as a sports writer for the newspaper of his high school where he excelled in football, earning an athletic grant-in-aid scholarship at Marshall University, where he played on the same Young Thundering Herd team featured in the Matthew McConaughey film "We Are Marshall."

Petras would later attend Kent State University studying journalism and public relations while working as a farm hand and janitor to support himself. He married his wife Debbie in 1975 and would not return to college until the autumn of 1985, supporting his young family, during that period joined with the addition of daughter Severine and son Robert Jr., by working various jobs at a fossil fuel power plant in Stratton, Ohio.

While working the coal fields of the power plant, Petras began writing during lunchbreaks and coffee breaks, authorized and unauthorized, and supplemented his income by penning freelance outdoor and sports stories for several local newspapers and regional magazines. He continued to hone his craft and eventually his prose and photography would earn print in numerous national publications, including *Field & Stream* and *Sports Afield.* In addition, he would score editorship with the regional magazines.

While averaging 50 hours a week at the power plant and authoring a dozen or more stories a month for local publications, Petras would continue pursuit of a Bachelor of Arts degree at West Liberty University, earning academic honors there and graduating in 1987.

During the early 1990s, Petras began writing fiction and scored some early success in the science fiction genre, etching his name on the highly esteemed "Locus Index of Science Fiction" with his contributions of " Charnel knowledge" in *Gaslight* and "Industrial Arts" in *Crossroads.* He would continue to earn publishing credits in a variety of fiction and nonfiction genres as well as experiencing success in poetry. To date, his work has seen print in more than 250 publications across the globe.

In August of 2022, Petras released his first book, "River Rats," a humorous collection of 25 coming-of-age stories based from the 1960s in his hometown Toronto, Ohio, a town he affectionately calls the Center of the Universe, where he and his wife Debbie still call home.

The longtime writer is also a certified personal fitness trainer, CrossFit Level 1 coach and nutritionist with numerous accredited specialties.

FOREWORD

Release the Belgium is a coming-of-age novella that takes place in the little eastern Ohio town of Toronto during 1965. You would not in any way confuse this Toronto for the one in Canada, especially in pronunciation; we longtime residents pronounce our hometown "Tronto," depending upon the time of night.

It is a town in which you can find a guy perching upon the same bar stool he did decades before and will go unoccupied during his absence. This kind of reverence can be found only in these rare, little, isolated pockets peopled with colorful characters.

RTB is a memoir weaved with some fiction such as "The Calling." Father Cappelli did not really sing like a bull that had just learned the meaning of mountain oyster. No, he sang much worse.

This memoir actually starts in the last chapter of my previous book, *River Rats*, in "The Seven-Day Blow," the beginning of my transition of transferring from a strict Catholic grade school to a stricter public junior high.

Some readers may maintain that a man nearing his 70th birthday jumping back into the skin and Converse sneakers of his 12- and-13-year-old self may seem creepy or overly nostalgic. But if I still feel some impact of the trauma that accompanies bullying, ostracizing, mental and physical abuse, underage substance abuse, racism and death—then I say *Release the Belgium* is a tale worth telling.

If I could best describe my style of writing, I could best describe it as "Little Animal House on the Prairie," with a little bit satire, a little bit dark humor and a whole lot karmic progression, this kind of karma not the wishful Western thinking that everyone gets their retribution sooner or later. No, I mean in the truest Eastern sense: that every action of everyone is connected in some way, related. By keeping this karmic progression in mind will help the reader to better understand what some may call a plot in *RTB*. But how can something be deemed a plot if it consists of a series of chronological true events in which I just happened to be one of the main characters?

The protagonist just happens to be me, a kid with a rebellious nature, a disposition he was most aware, and yet, paradoxically, he did not rebel against this nature. No wonder being 13 years old is such a confusing age.

Some names have been changed, only a few; and some events I have borrowed from other periods, just a couple, but I own them, paid for by my own experience, blood, sweat and nervous system, and I keep them on a palette of colors from which I can portray my stories any time I choose.

I don't truly know whether the pen is mightier than the sword, but I can tell you the writer gets in the last word and that last word should come in the form of dance if the story is truly to have a happy ending, ideally a conga line because, yes, I believe we are all connected in one way or another.

After the ending of *Release*, I included six short stories in *A T-town City Six Pack*. I hope you find them as fun as reading as I did writing.

Come join me in this conga line called life; everyone leads, everyone follows, the dance of the full circle.

Robert E. Petras Sr.

RELEASE THE BELGIUM

When I was a kid, I didn't know a Belgium from a cheese Danish. All I knew it was something as peculiar to T-town City as were bumper skiing, river rats, corning and toboggans, the wool knitted kind, not to be confused with the wooden recurved thingy we called *bobsled*.

I would soon learn a toboggan was today's equivalent of smart phone GPS: It marked foul lines, goal lines, other boundaries and a Belgium. A Belgium, I suppose, substituted for a flag, something our families couldn't afford. If they could, our mothers would have cut it to size for curtains, or worse, school clothes.

The first Belgium originated in the Mill Row District of T-town, supposedly invented by fourth-grade prodigy Dave Hudok, who successfully answered Brussels as the capital of Belgium on a geography test while all 39 of his classmates guessed it was some other vegetable. The alternative story of origin maintained that Dave's academic prowess for state capitals and vegetables came as a result of his wearing a special thinking cap, a toboggan made in the country where waffles originated.

Thanks to Hudy, the game of Release the Belgium was first released in the Millrow, spread throughout the south end of town, crossed the Mason-Dixon Line called Main Street, spilled into the North End, where evolved a brass-tactics version that included brass knuckles and brass-pleated billy clubs.

Outside of T-town exist watered-down versions of Release the Belgium, especially the sophomoric one widely known as Capture the Flag, or simply Capture. The only version to capture the unflagging spirit of T-town City sophistication and intellect was and shall always be Release the Belgium, often known as RTB or merely Release.

You had only two teams in RTB back then: the good guys and the bad guys. In T-town City sometimes called Toronto, Ohio, or

T-town for short; good was bad; bad, good. The objective of the contest, of course, was to capture the flag of your opponent, in most cases, a toboggan, even if a dude was wearing it. Defenses usually stuck the toboggan on a stick, or dangled it from a tree branch in plain view, in the middle of a mosquito-infested swamp or just plain, ordinary everyday quicksand.

In most dialects of T-townese, including Southender and Northend Hunky, *release* means capture, and vice-versa, or just plain vice.

To increase your chances to capture or release the coveted cap, you wanted to capture as many opponents as possible and throw them in jail but not release them. Teams could range anywhere from four to 20 players, averaging about the roster size of your typical T-town sandlot football game, minus the steady quarterback.

To capture enemies, you needed to chase them down, ambush them from a bush, trap them in a camouflaged pit, or swoop down from a tree like a Jocko spotting an unfinished stogie. Outside in the elements, the element of surprise was most effective and then muscle or guts was needed to dislodge the enemy from their advance or defensive positions, and once dislodged or knocked out, you then would escort the would-be crooks by the crooks of the elbow and march them to the site of confinement. The counter-strategy to this strategy was to outrun, outflank or outsmart the lackadaisical sentries or lack of sentries guarding the jail, this makeshift structure usually made up of a horseshoe of bushes, rocks or jagged cliffs, accessible by only monkey vine or bribes; the Jocko Twins, Bobby and Mike, often open to a contribution or two to their ongoing Stunt-Your-Growth Fund.

Then, as in tag-team studio wrestling, you needed to free your team members by slapping each one's palms, and they would be out like ten Three Stooges. In the north end version, slapping the jailers usually freed them from their senses.

Sometimes, you needed to employ old Indian tricks, like misdirecting owl hoots or tossing rocks, six or seven of the latter usually enough to flatten and dent the toboggan-donning jailkeeper's cranium into a Belgium waffle—come to think of it, a possible source of origin of this most wholesome game.

The jailkeeper generally perused girlie mags a few feet in front of the unlucky horseshoe while the prison guards positioned themselves 30 or so feet from the jail. The north end version of Release included the bail bondsman, generally positioned in a Market Street office eight miles away in Steubenville.

With enough players on your side, you could post a scout or two, like Coner Sloane, the best tree climber in the history of T-town City. Oaks, maples, monkey ball trees--Coner could make a crow's nest out of any treetop and with eager eyes could pinpoint the tip of a toboggan tassel from 400 yards away and tip off his team captain by using a series of hooty-hoot-hoots and other sophisticated spy craft. This captain could be, say, Chuckie Rex, who would just shake his head from side to side and say, "You just can't make this kind of shit up," and would then make up a strategy by poking holes in the soft earth with a stick and etch in all directions how to outflank your outflanking enemy, using sandlot football plays like the old triple reverse, double throwback with a quadruple crisscross block.

Speaking of sophisticated spy craft, we south enders often employed the services of the Twins Conlon, identical from the tips of their Keds to the tips of their toboggans, except after looking at them about 3000 times, you could see Bobby had been born with a more prominent fuck-you smirk than Mike. Still, few kids could tell them apart; few could pull them apart, especially when they had mild disagreements regarding the ethics of spy craft and then they would duel it out with double dukes. They could jump ship faster than a river rat hopscotching across Ohio River driftwood, even when grounded. Always changing sides, changing clothes, exchanging top secret information, smokes and passwords, they made the ideal double agents and were only caught when they happened to be spying for the same team. You could never outjockey a Jocko.

11

Winning RTB took a total team effort, defensively and offensively, following stick strategy to a T-town T. You needed fearless, reckless rushers like Yankee Yaskanich, who had an uncanny grip strength, what he called the *clam*. Yank was the original tree hugger and if some arch-enemy were about to capture him, Yank would hug a tree trunk with all of his clam-strength. The only way you could yank Yankee from an oak, maple or monkey ball tree was to fell it with your official Boy Scout axe, drag him away by the ankles, and with any luck topple crow-nesting Coner to the turf on top of him.

George Miller and I manned the freelance position, basically because we could never remember Chuck's intricate dirt playbook, but by giving each other some little gestures, like a little tug on the lower lip, we would know what each other was going to do without saying a word. George would fake out the enemy with a fake rush to draw them away just as we had drawn in the soft dirt in our gray matter while I would do a real rush around their flanks and provide George cover by tossing several tactical monkey balls, and George would fake out his flank; then we would release the Belgium and rescue any damsels in distress, but we seemed damned in the damsel-rescue-saving business.

Nearly all rules of Release the Belgium were unwritten and as far as anyone knows still remain unwritten to this day. Contests could be staged anywhere: in the woods, the parks, ballfields, river banks, even alleys and streets. Declaring the winner varied from locale to locale. The most acceptable declaration resulted from simply snatching the Belgium before the defenders trampled you to a well-done waffle, and then you held the trophy aloft like a bloody scalp, some of it already clotting. The north end version mandated you had to transport the Belgium to the capturer's home front in one piece but not necessarily the capturer.

Those playground battles often ended in a draw no matter how much blood was drawn, the first glow of street lamps ending the contests, and then the self-designated team crier would cry so all the neighborhood could hear, "Ollie, Ollie, in come free, last one in is a gummy boy!" a T-townese adaptation for "Olly, Olly oxen free!"

And one by one by one, we would clamber, jostle, shuffle, saunter, jog, sprint or limp under the soft solace of amber lights to our postgame banquets of hash or meatloaf, face grounding or some other serious time punishment before the infamous time-out was invented if we so much as missed the home curfew by seconds.

I have 13 acres of prime Appalachian forest filled with lots of climbing trees; hugging ones, too; oaks, maples and a monkey ball as well as caves, cliffs, crags and boulders the size of a Volkswagen van and other cool hiding places, and we can choose sides the old reliable way with an "Eeny meeny miney moe catch a Hudy by the toe," or chant the old one-potato-two-potato song and re-release Release the Belgium. Bring a toboggan or two, the wooly knitted kind, and we shall have more fun and excitement than you can shake a strategy stick at.

Last one in is a gummy boy.

FAST-TWITCH JEANS

The ACTN3 gene provides instructions for making a protein called alpha-actinin-3, which is predominantly found in fast-twitch muscle fibers.—*MedicinePlus*

I didn't know at the time I had fast-twitch genes. I thought fast-twitch jeans was something Elvis wore.

I was in sixth grade, my last month at St. Francis School, and walking somewhere with Timmy Maple and Dennis Cich, both eighth graders. Out of the streaked Windex blue sky, we decided to a play game in which two opponents grappled standing upright until someone tumbled to the grass, in this case, the grass growing between the cracks in the concrete. We were wrestling on the south sidewalk on Jefferson Street, the block directly below the T-town City public swimming pool.

Being two years younger, I was called out first. Then Tim or Dennis would face off from me, our hands resting upon each other's shoulders as though we were going to do a cowboy slow dance, and then try to knock each other off our feet. All I did was whip a leg behind their calves, pushed their chests and faster than you can say "faster than you can say" they went down like the first domino in a one-thousand-domino script Ohio domino chain. I won like 63 consecutive matches using my patented leg whip until a couple high school goons came along with some patented moves of their own and left their trademarks on my face when, finally, my butt cheeks kissed the concrete canvas.

I might have had fast-twitch muscles at an early age, but I needed years for my brain cells to catch up.

I was always bugging the neighborhood high school guys like Toot Nordberg, Ed Chambers, John Skrabak and Pudge Vogelmore to play football with me. I remember one autumn day at Pudge's front lawn when the leaves of the shag bark hickory tree marking the goal line in his front yard were starting to turn golden and Pudge

14

was clinging on to a regulation white football endorsed by Sammy Baugh while I was clinging on to one of Pudge's ankles like a regulation ball-and-chain endorsed by the Field Boss at the Mansfield State Pen. Up and down the field Pudge went, plowing furrows into the Vogelmore lawn with my elbows, knees and chin, scoring something like six times on just one carry. When my turn to play offense came, Pudge would scoop me up and run with me back and forth, tamping down the divots.

I like to believe this type of exercise gave Pudge the leg drive to become the punter for the Toronto Red Knights football team.

I was in sixth grade and shagging punts for Pudge at the south end of the junior high school, S.C. Dennis. Pudge was booming tight spirals high enough to pierce the Ohio Valley pollution, balls that I was snagging despite all my fingers one by one becoming stubbed while the middle of my chest was growing a third nipple from the impact of the leather meteor. Then Pudge's ball-and-chain leg launched one that appeared to sail toward the cornstalks of Sloane's farm, and I whirled around to chase the rpm-ing ball when suddenly my forehead played two-hand tab with an upright on a solid steel goal post. Splitting the upright with my two foreheads left me with a splitting headache and a lump the size of a hand grenade. When I looked at the mirror at home, I appeared to have stood on my head in a minefield.

Sixth grade constituted the tender years for me, especially when considering my face was consistently being tenderized. My buddy Joe Sokol and I were at S.C. Dennis, this time at the opposite end of the field, opposite his brother Mike, who was a junior in high school. Mike yelled out the old next-touchdown-wins rule despite being already up by five touchdowns while standing three yards from the next.

Mike hiked the ball to himself, took a step back and then bowled toward us as though he were going to knock down every pin on all 16 alleys at T-town Lanes, and Joe, the consummate team player, let me get a chance for all the glory as he wobbled away like an unrulily

15

seven pin while Mike was seeing red, the red of winning a free game at midnight bowling, with me the red head pin. I went low, my forehead connecting with a high-stepping kneecap that felt more like a hubcap attached to a '63 Chevy coating Franklin Street with two streaks of Firestone.

Fortunately, my lips and eye softened the blow somewhat. My face looked like one of those dudes who say, "I'll fight you with both of my hands tied behind my back," and the other dude took him up on it.

Mike fell shy of the goal line by the length of a detached nose.

So, I went to school the next day, one side of my face looking like Franklin Street after a Saturday night. All the boys were asking me who kicked my ass. Joe, of course, had my back and told everybody that a public schoolgirl named B.J. did it because I was throwing lead sinkers at her down upon a beached barge on the river bank at the mouth of Jeddo Run and that the only reason she did not give me a wedgie up to where my ears used to sit was because Joe asked if she would be my baby shakes.

So now I had the stigma of being wedgied up by a girl my age while going steady with someone I would not touch with ten board feet of treated Scotch pine from Coopers Hardware, unless, of course, I had to defend myself. Then again, there was the looming threat of Mother Mary Paula and her straight-edged ruler from Kuhn's Hardware, just a lead sinker toss away from St. Francis School. If Mother had learned so much as half an ass cheek had been kicked while on school property, she would have rapped my knuckles all the way down to both hemispheres of my ass.

I could take a punishment better than I could take a joke, maybe because I hated losing and kids would poke fun at me.

They would make fun of your clothes, they would make fun of your looks, your lunch bucket, your bike, your fishing pole. They would make fun of your first name, your last name. They would call you names. They would make fun of your family, your family car. If you could afford one, they would make fun of your yacht. They would make fun of your house, your sisters, your grandmother's moustache. And when they used up all your personal shortcomings, they would make some up. They would say you liked some girl whom you had never met; they would say you kissed this girl in a funky kind of way; they would even stoop so low to say you kissed sideways.

I was finishing up the last few weeks of my stay at St. Francis School. It was spring, pastel flowers popping out everywhere, everything as green as go. Love was everywhere, and one public school kid my age would have loved to rearrange my face. Chuckie Darwin stood a couple of inches taller than I and outweighed me by a good twenty pounds. All spring I had been avoiding Chuckie like someone who had swindled the nuns out of Pagan Baby money.

Chuckie lived near the top of Banfield Avenue, residing about a block and a half away from my residence on Biltmore. Chuckie blocked all paths leading to my friends outside my neighborhood. I found a way to outflank this troll trolling Ridge and Banfield by cutting through the woods and then slanting across the Little League ball park.

One day after school, the troll popped out of nowhere as trolls do—on top of the grassy knoll next to the tennis courts, cutting me off like a steel goal post.

Up close, standing below Chuckie, I now understood I had underestimated him; he stood at least an inch taller than I had previously thought and was sprouting a five o'clock shadow. But it wasn't happy hour for me.

Darwin was square looking all over. He had a square jaw and his dark crew cut made his angular face appear even squarer, like a robot's.

"Well, if it ain't Peaches, the Hunky boy," he said, his voice even square.

If he continued working his way down the list of all my shortcomings, I had a long time remaining on earth. I wanted to tell

17

him technically I was half-Irish, with a little German coming from both sides of the family. I wanted to tell him I was adopted, that I was a descendent of Paul Revere.

"Hi, Chuckie," was all I could say.

"You know why I am here, Peaches?"

"No idea," I said.

"I heard you said that you can take me," he said.

Take him where? I didn't even have enough money to take myself out for take-out. I was so strapped for cash I couldn't have beaten Chuckie with invisible leather.

"You start it and I'll finish it, Peaches."

He wrapped one arm behind his back, waved the other one in front of my face as if to show he had no foreign objects up his sleeveless T-shirt. "I'll fight you with one arm tied behind my back," he said, looking me squarely in the eyes.

"I never said that I could take you," I said.

"Are you calling me a liar?"

He had me on a technicality. He was lying out his square teeth. I was weighing my options, like placing an order for one last square meal, although I suspected the only thing Chuckie was serving was hairy knuckle sandwiches complemented with a wedge of wedgie.

"I don't feel like fighting today," I said.

Then he shoved me, two hands by my count.

I didn't budge. Neither did he.

He shoved me again. This time, I grabbed him by the hand that was supposed to be behind his back, whirled him around and flung him to the ground. I leaped upon his chest, knees pressing it, and then punched him square on his square jaw, soon followed by a short round of round houses.

"I give up," he squeaked. "I give."

I pushed myself off him, stood, and then looked down at Chuckie, blubbering.

His face looked as though it were just introduced to Mike Sokol and Mike was wearing brass kneecaps.

I wanted to pull him up by the wedgie. I wanted to tell him "Yes, I can take you and not only did I take you to Glass Jaw but on a tour of the entire glass works and made you make a donation to the I Give Society!" I wanted to tell him that he was a big, fat liar mouth. Most of all I just wanted to go home.

After Chuckie left, I wiped my hands on my jeans; my legs were shaking. When I returned home, after walking the direct way for the first time in a long while, down Ridge up Biltmore, my legs were still twitching. I could have clipped another 63 wrestlers to the ground by the time the spasms subsided.

With Chuckie out of the way, I thought I had free passage again through the south end streets of town. Then a bucket brigade of rumors hit B.J. like a ton of toxic projectiles. She had forgiven me for tossing lead sinkers at her. Most of all, she loved the thought of being called *baby shakes* and looked very much forward to doing something so kinky as kissing sideways.

HALFTIME

Halftime—what the Conlon twins Bobby and Mike and I called Holy Communion. We might have given it a moniker relating to football, but, in reality, this period was more like the five-complete-innings rule—say from a rainout—to make a regulation baseball game in order to count in the standings, a technicality that would prevent us from committing a sin that would leave a stench in the soul as foul as Satan's shithouse and make you spend eternity shoveling it with a rubber spoon.

At halftime, the twins and I would be out of St. Francis of Assisi Church faster than you could say "transubstantiation," if you could say "transubstantiation."

Ronnie Paris was ringing the bronze hand bell that signaled everybody to get ready to receive the Body of Christ. Ronnie replaced me as Joe Sokol's altar boy partner. Joe was *Leave It to Beaver's* Eddie Haskell in a black and white cassock. Ronnie was Joe's latest altar flunky. Even while slouching from the back pew, I could see Joe leaning ever so slightly toward Ronnie and mutter out the side of his mouth, "Your dick is sticking out." Only a trained ear well versed in whispered church scatology and a former Joe Sokol flunky could have detected the slightest pause before Ronnie should have started clanging the bell, this miscue caused by the inner cringe one senses when one's genitals are the source of display in front of 300 parishioners and the Holy Spirit.

Then came the moment when mere bread from Gregory's Bakery, south two blocks and a sliced bread toss away, became the body of Jesus Christ, the equivalent of five completed innings to declare halftime.

The trick, of course, was to skedaddle a one-Mississippi-one count after consecration before Father Cappelli, facing the crucified Jesus, wheeled around and took a headcount. Sometimes, Father paused for dramatic effect, then heeled around and caught you in the

20

act and his face would suddenly have the look he just lost money betting on Notre Dame. He would give you the stink eye the next time he saw you cowering in the nether pews, a look promising a posse of nuns to run you down, marshaled by none other than Mother Mary Paula.

You had a better chance of winning the lottery and being struck by lightning in the same day than you did escaping the gnarly talons of this wing-footed, wimpled wonder. Mother Mary Paula was half coon hound, half greyhound and half-crazy and always up for a full-blown chase after parochial school fugitive.

To this day, I can only speculate on why Mother had it out for Stanley Chesney. She had a tolerance for schoolboy shenanigans about as thin as a nun's tan line, and she would pounce on you at the drop of a habit, or in this case, pencils. Maybe Mother was pissed at Stan because he tripped the trip wire separating *clumsy* from *curious,* dropping the lead seven times, a new catechism class record. Maybe she was so pissed because of the nonchalant way Stan retrieved the standard issue yellow number 2 Dixon-Ticonderoga from the freshly waxed red-and-black checkered linoleum. The way he took his good, old time you would have thought Stash had discovered a stash of *National Geographics* under the desk of Ann Lamantia.

Mother Mary Paula scowled in a way that only could be done by someone's face framed in black executioner's cloth.

Stan was not so nonchalant dashing outside the classroom into the hall outside onto the playground, Mother giving chase, her habit flapping behind her like the Jolly Rodger, a steel-edged ruler in one boney fist, the other fist chugging like a crap shooter pleading to the gambling gods that grandma needs a new pair of shoes. I was pretty certain Mother was going to kick the crap out of Stash with her sensible square-toed shoes. It was snake eyes for Stan.

Stanley had wiry chestnut hair and a keg for a chest and was stubby-legged, this posture giving him such a low center of gravity you would think he was running on all fours. He could hug corners like a river rat and scamper in unpredictable directions. Across Findlay Street onto the convent lawn they dashed. They wrapped around the nunnery a couple of times. I think some hedges were hopped, and Stan was doing the unthinkable—extending his lead by a good straight-edged ruler length—and back across Findlay sprinted Stash followed by the one-nun posse and into the sacred confines of the church they went. All the while I am thinking "You can't buy this kind of entertainment anywhere." I didn't think the level of entertainment could be any better than what the forty of us enrapt sixth graders were watching through the vinegar-and-water-smeared multi-paned picture windows, amusement we hadn't enjoyed since a few weeks before when Stan tried to seek sanctuary in the boys restroom, *lavatory* the nuns called it, getting Stash on a semantic technicality. This time Stan sought refuge in the most sacrosanct edifice of all—a Roman Catholic church, off limits to authorities of any kind, including law enforcement, the military, demons, the repo man, vampires, door to door salesmen, bill collectors, bounty hunters, irate wives.

But not to nuns. And nunbane had not been discovered yet. Mother Mary Paula, utilizing half her canine pedigree, treed Stan atop the pipes of the organ in the choir loft.

The black-robed bounty hunter was soon back holding Stash by the scruff of his neck. I was wrong about the previous entertainment value. You couldn't have smoked all the amusement that was coming next. Mother gave Stanley an earful of Holy Spirit-approved expletives as well as an assful of welts. A few minutes or so of entertaining us, she was flagging; her famed left rearing back only half-mast and bearing down only half-assed on Stanley's dupa. Mother Mary Paula was huffing and puffing like a big bad wolf who had smoked one too many Tareytons, and Stanley's butt rated good for a category 4 hurricane. Mother paused in her ass assault. Beading upon her brow were beads of sweat the size of the Our Father beads on her rosary. She had a look on her face suggesting she needed to throw some type of pugilistic Hail Mary to save her unbeaten streak of subduing 137 parochial school fugitives. She turned around and looked at the enraptured audience and said in a voice as crusty as the garbage bin outside Gregory's: "Let this be a lesson to you all." Then she taught us the word *ambidextrous*.

Looking back, Stan could have used a good pair of fast-twitch jeans, at least ones with a padded ass.

The Conlons and I, safe from a horde of ninja nuns and the most holy stink eye of Father Cappelli and from spending an eternity spooning with sinners, were soon ensconced upon the pivoting red vinyl stools of Melhorns's Dairy, a mom and pop place where we indulged in after-church-services pop, and maybe a Tareyton or two, joined by others of the absent halftime headcount--Tim Maple, Dennis Cich, Chuckie Rex, Bobeen Daughtery. We always joked about Melhorn's being a church, that we attended Sunday Mass at St. Lou's. After much time and reflection, Mr. Lou Melhorn must have been a saint tolerating us merry band of south enders.

THE CALLING

I was no longer serving as an altar boy because I was scheduled to attend public school in the fall. If you were Catholic and attended or transferred to a public school, the nuns thought they were punishing you by banishing you from your altar boy privileges-- as if Catholic schoolboys were arm wrestling one another for first rights to awaken an hour before everyone else did so that they could hold a paten below the chins of 300 snotty nosed kids, hoping just one time Father Cappelli would slip up and drop the Holy Eucharist and you just might bump a boob on the way down to save the Host; and Father was working on the all-time halftime record of most consecutive servings without an error.

I think the nuns thought by banning public school heathens from serving they were giving us a little taste of what it would be like excommunicated, or a Methodist.

About the only thing I was going to miss about altar-boying was the lighting and extinguishing of candles, before and after mass, especially with Joseph Martin Sokol. We used this thing that looked like some bronze medieval weapon that needed two hands and some plumbers words to maneuver. This implement had a wick for lighting and a cup for extinguishing. This bludgeon measured six feet from the end of the ornamental handle to the tip of the war end, I suppose because the loose garments altar boys traditionally wore were fire hazards, and altar boys were hard to replace in a minute's notice.

Back then, we called altar-boying *serving*. As we were changing into our un-fireproofed altar boy apparel prior to serving, Joe and I would goose each other with those firebrands, when the other wasn't looking, which wasn't often, or empty handed, which wasn't often, either.

On school days, all eight grades of St. Francis had to assemble by individual classes in church for the 8:15. Kids would arrive by foot, by car, by bus, bicycle, never at once. If we arrived early enough before the 8:15, Joe and I would be out on the altar near the communion rails wielding those war implements as the first students trickled inside from the side doors and then turned a corner by the pay-all-you-can votive candles. Joe would thrust his firebrand right over the communion rail and goose an unsuspecting girl with the bronze cup—if he was accurate—and she would jump, her face turning as red as the glass encasing the votive candles, and she would turn every which way searching for the source while Joe muttered just loud enough so only the girl and I could hear, "I can feel the presence of the Holy Ghost," and then go about his altar boy duties looking as though goosing a girl's spiritual gizzard was the last thing on his mind.

The girl then went to her designated pew, kneeled upon the kneeler, made the sign of the cross, and she would start squirming, a smile on her face proclaiming she was prepared for the second coming.

Thanks to being one of those public-school heathens, I was no longer a participant but an observer to all kinds of entertainment you could find only in our church.

During this particular mass, I was already in halftime position, half the time my ass resting on the pew to allow the blood to return to my knees after pressing them to the steel-reinforced cushion some Catholics called a kneeler. By the end of the first quarter—the Epistle—three-quarters of the parish had already assumed the half-ass disguise of kneeling, including the elderly and those eager to get the hell out of there. Of course, there was always a handful of school kids and the elderly that attempted to make it through the entire mass with their kneecaps kissing the kneecapping kneeler. Watching them squirm as if goosed by the Holy Ghost was entertainment worthy of contributing to the collection basket. There were those who must have thought they were on some kind of fidget budget and by exceeding the limit they would have to pay exorbitant interest rates of time in purgatory, and they would try to alleviate their knee fatigue and aching lower back by moaning and groaning and whimpering to which Father must have thought they were poking fun of his singing by giving him a dose of his own ear medicine.

To me, I wanted the full use and support of my knees to get out of church by halftime as fast as I could. I still did not trust the possibility of a posse of nuns lassoing me with their abnormally long rosaries. And the icons of calves painted upon the walls of church constantly reminded us of the rumors that Mother Mary Paula starred in the rodeo before she got the calling.

Catholics probably figured out since St. Peter was the first pope that as long as you made only three points of contact you performed a legal kneel in the eyes of God, provided your folded hands were visible to the tabernacle, even if your kneel more resembled that of the downward dog pose—your ass pointing to high heaven.

This half-kneel would create the domino effect. If the person in front of you would assume this pose, you, in turn, would have to duplicate it lest you wanted his ass and the reminder of his last meal inches away from your nose the remainder of the service or, in my case, halftime. Your half-ass effort would force the would-be kneelers behind you to park their asses to the wood—all the way to the very last pew in church. If you were staring down from the balcony and saw such a scene it would look like football fans at the stadium doing the wave—ass first.

Father Angelo J. Cappelli, A. J. for short, was of modest height and built, with skin so olive you would have thought his mother's maiden name was Martini. He had a bull-sized cowlick over which his tar-pitched hair curled across an eyebrow, giving A.J. a perpetual WTF look; and he sported a nose you could only give due tribute with an ode. There were color portraits of our church pastor on every school room wall depicting him with his monster cowlick slicked down with Italian axle grease. His black eyes in this photo would follow you no matter where you goofed off in the classroom.

Like a lot of priests, Father Cappelli liked to put on a singing show. Despite a voice that bellowed like a bull that just learned the meaning of mountain oyster, Father bellowed away as though effort earned him extra credits in his piety rating. The only musical bone in his body was his nose, an organ he blew frequently upon the altar, and judging by its tone and size it could have been the result of a surgical graph between a shin bone and a trombone supported by a frame that was one-hundred-percent boneless ham.

That Nostrildamus had a cold and smoked two packs a day didn't help this particular performance of Agnus Dei. Agnus Die in Latin means *lamb of God,* but A.J. must have thought it meant *mutton* and he was butchering the hell out of it. Not only were kids my age bolting from the deli, but also adults, including the organist, some pressing their ears.

We would not have been paying much attention to Father Cappelli even if he were celebrating mass in American slang. He machine-gunned his Latin prayers as if he were running late for a poker game. For all I knew, he could have been calling us *a bunch of jackoffs;* after all, he was privy to that type of info inside the confessional booth.

At the altar, whenever Father faced the delegation, Joe would kneel upon that red carpet behind him so straight and angelic, hands folded perfectly, eyes cast heavenward, you would have thought the nuns had finally got to Joe and shoved a holy-water-treated board up his ass, but the moment father turned his attention to the tabernacle, Joe started squirming as if that board were rotten and infested with worms.

And when father sang like the cows coming home, we took off for greener countertops.

Your halftime habits and everything you held dear and unholy could all change in a T-town tick if you got hit by the calling. The calling is when the Holy Spirit holds a raffle with every Catholic boy's name on a ticket thrown into a pointy hat and then pulls out the one with your name and you would dedicate yourself to the priesthood.

27

The calling could hit you anytime, anywhere. You could be standing at home plate with two outs and bases loaded, your team down three runs, the bases full and the T-town Little League championship on the line or you could be up in the balcony of the Manos Theatre with some girl, squeezing the shit out of her Charmin, and if the Holy Spirit pulled your raffle ticket, you would drop the bat and wouldn't give a shit about your main squeeze and instead go right down the path of righteousness.

When old enough, you would take the midnight train to the seminary and give up cussing, girlie magazines and reduce your daily output of impure thoughts from a couple hundred a day to a more manageable number.

Mother Augustine often gave the Holy Spirit the name the Caller, and when the Caller made a house call you couldn't have kept him out with a bake sale and a magazine subscription drive. It's as if the statue of St. Francis standing in the back of church suddenly came to life and stepped off his little foot step to give you a guaranteed-for-lifetime wedgie with his rosary beads.

If you were too young to attend the seminary, you would pass the time pretending to give out Holy Communion with hosts made from stale Wonder Bread to friends and family and hearing confessions from Ann and DeeDee Lamantia and give them a proper penance. You would write sermons instead of reading comic books and even ground your parents if you thought they weren't coughing up enough dough for the collection basket. You would go around town baptizing heathens, like your Methodist cousins, with any source of water available, spit on them if you had to, then convert them to grow up rooting for Notre Dame. You would perform last rites—Extreme Unction—on kids taking a tumble on the playground or a fist. You would wear nothing except black clothes, including your gauchies, and people would mistake you for a young Johnny Cash, changing their tune when you sang "Ring of Fire" word for word in perfect Latin.

It was after halftime one Sunday when the calling came calling at Melhorn's Dairy. We called the establishment St. Lou's after the owner Lou Melhorn, who had to put up with Dennis Cich, Tim Maple, Teddy Elson and me this morning. Lou was getting up in the years, and time, gravity and goof-offs were slowly taking him down. Lou was starting to look like a turtle outside his shell. He had a voice that squeaked like a wooden screw too big for its hole and the angrier Lou became at us for screwing around the squeakier it became and finally on this Sunday Lou pointed toward the exit and squeaked, "I've had enough. All you do is come here to drink one bottle of pop and smoke cigarettes behind your mothers' backs. Now get the hell out of here!"

In his tribute to us, Lou failed to mention those cigarettes we were smoking behind our mothers' backs came from the back shelves of St. Lou's. Anyhow, Hell couldn't have been any smokier than the ledge upon we were sitting moments later in front of the dairy's big picture window; we were puffing away as though it were New Year's Day and the day before Lent all rolled in one.

The four of us had long been practicing the T-town art of cupping. If some suspicious adult like a teacher, parent or football coach approached our smokers den, we would pinch the smoldering smoke with the tips of our booger picker and opinion finger and curl the cigarette under the lampshade of a palm. Some smoke would still waft out, but this maneuver was usually adequate enough to conceal our underaged habit to fool a passing motorist, whom we would wave to with the other hand.

On the other hand, sometimes someone would surprise us by turning the corner of the sidewalk on foot and we would have to palm our cigarettes between our teeth, our lips pressed together tighter than Superglued Tupperware.

Turning a corner on foot was none other than full-time priest and part-time church attendance truant officer and wannabe opera singer, A.J. Cappelli, a Pall Mall of his own dangling from his church-wine drinking lips. Fortunately, three of us were not

29

smoking. Unfortunately, Teddy was. Fortunately, Teddy was the most skilled with the mouth-palming technique.

If you knew what to look for as I did, you could detect a little orange light glowing through the skin of Teddy's cheeks, an illumination similar to the one whenever the Holy Spirit leaves his business card. Maybe Father saw what I saw. Maybe he saw Teddy as some kind of jack o-lantern who would be best decorating some dormitory in a reform school.

"I somehow missed you at the altar receiving communion this morning," Father said, reeking of incense and Pall Malls.

"We helped some little old lady crossing the street," I said, using the frequently used good deed Boys Scouts often pulled out of their butts as an excuse for showing up late at meetings and not completing their work to move up the ranks leading to Eagle Scout and also at grade school for failing to turn in homework. "She gave us some fudge and we didn't want to hurt her feelings by not eating some."

I had fudged the truth, well maybe the whole recipe. Back then, eating food or drinking something other than your own spit within an hour of receiving the Blessed Sacrament was a sin as serious as leaving mass before halftime and could put you at the back of the long waiting list to get out of purgatory.

Teddy just stood there staring ahead, his lips stuck together like two strips of Duct Tape, and he was ducking all of Father's questions with the old silent act.

"What's a matter, Theodore, cat's got your tongue?"

"Theodore got the calling, Father," I said, "and he has taken up the vow of silence."

Father looked Teddy up and down as if he were sizing him up for a cassock and collar while Teddy kept getting so stiff you would have thought Duct Tape poisoning was setting in.

Teddy was a year or two younger than I. He had short brown hair as stiff as a used wire brush and a smattering of freckles, enough to give him a deceiving appearance of innocence. Teddy was also a third-year Tenderfoot who got into some trouble at summer Boy Scout camp when the camp director caught Teddy smoking and it wasn't from some mishap that occurred during Cooking Merit Badge Class. That Teddy kept puffing away as though he were giving a seminar on smoke signals didn't send any mixed signals that Teddy took his role of camp clown seriously.

Father Cappelli gave Teddy the once over a couple of times.

As punishment, the camp director made Teddy recite the Scout pledge and 12 laws in front of the entire mess hall before supper— a couple of hundred in all, including a few very high-ranking Scout officials. Of course, Teddy no more knew the Scout oath and 12 laws than he would his altar boys prayers and the 12 commandments, much to the amusement of most of my troop, but not to a couple of scoutmasters and the other 14 troops in attendance. The only one more speechless than Teddy was the camp director, just standing up there, his lower lip quivering as if it were stuck inside the spokes of a bicycle and he wasn't the kind of spokesman who had words for this kind of mess inside a mess hall. If you had seen Teddy up there in front of the mess hall, his lips pressed tight, you would have thought the Calling conveniently hit him right then and there.

When he finally collected himself and Teddy by the cuff of an arm, the camp director assigned Teddy as further punishment to mess hall duty scrubbing pots and pans and toilets until Teddy learned the Boy Scout doctrines or quit smoking, whatever came first. One thing led to another and that another was that Teddy pissed in the camp Kool-Aid. Teddy's tenure in the Boy Scouts was pretty much kumbaya after that.

Teddy once again was at center stage and getting the once over again. Father kept circling Teddy all the while saying some Glory Bes and a prayer he must have made up on the spot in Latin, but I recognized *nincompoop,* which every Catholic schoolboy knew as a nice Catholic way of saying *asshole*. "It's a miracle," Father kept muttering between signing the cross and puffing his nonfiltered down to the nub. "A miracle when I would have settled for a simple transfer to another state."

Father stared in Teddy's nearly lifeless brown eyes and said," Stop by the rectory this afternoon and we shall talk about it."

The little life Teddy did have remaining in his brown eyes seemed to say, "I might be holding my breath, but don't hold yours."

Then Father went inside St. Lou's and we skedaddled faster than you can say, "second half!"

SOUL TWINKERS

Back when I played Little League baseball, we didn't line up after a game and high-five our opponents. If anybody did high-five anybody, it was to the jaw behind five knuckles.

Uttering "nice game" or any of the like was considered a sign of weakness, a gesture of submission. If your parents had brought you up right, you would have uttered "you stink," or the more emphatic "you suck," or the ultimate as John *Yankee* Yaskanich often hollered "You losers stink like suck," even if his team just lost 31-0.

They didn't award participation trophies back then. They awarded you boobie prizes, rewarded some poor dupa for recording the most called third strikes on him with his bat resting on his shoulders or for letting the most fly balls drop for errors, and they gave you something appropriate or symbolic like a toilet plunger or used spittoon, and you would go through life accepting that you sucked.

Sportsmanship was a practice reserved for the coaches, and no greater display of sportsmanship was exhibited than the T-town City Little League contest between the Lions Club and T.L. *T.L.* stood for *Toronto Lanes,* but every kid under the age of 41 called them the *Titty Lickers,* and one afternoon they were led by slugger Frank Slowikowski, and they were out to put a good, old-fashioned licking on the everybody's arch-rival, the Lions Club.

From the parents down to the players, the Lions were about as well liked as a den of repo men. They were cheap shot nickel-and-dimers who would take the ice cream right of a kid's hand if he so much as came up a penny short or one inch shy. They would take over the bleachers with their cowbells and fog horns; and whenever one of their kids did something well, like get a base hit, catch the ball or blow his nose, they tooted their horns as though these stuck-ups were God's gift to winning and had golden trumpets stuck up their asses. If a kid on the opposing team would strike out, boot a ground ball or shit himself sliding into base, they would cackle like an orgy in a hen house.

An old T-town saying is "The monkey ball doesn't fall too far from the tree," and no team exemplified this saying more than the Lions players themselves. Mentored by their cheap shot fathers, the players were so cheap they wouldn't pay their opponents a compliment. The few times they would lose, the Lions coaches and players attributed a loss to their ace pitcher's having a sore arm, or the other team was just plain lucky, or that the umpire needed glasses or new ones.

The Lions players always had their noses stuck up in the air as if their boogers were all-you-can-eat McNuggets. If they got thrown out at base, they would come up limping, or if they struck out, they would stare at the bat for a few seconds and then cuss out the bat boy.

The Fros-T-Cream, a T-town City ice cream parlor, awarded any Little Leaguer who hit a legitimate home run a king-sized ice cream cone, chocolate or vanilla, the 25-center—a value those days equivalent to two Snickers bars, two boxes of Lemonheads and one Cherry Blend cigar; the waffle cone itself the size of a four-cell flashlight and probably longer lasting. Ever ready, Frank the Tank rubbed his hands in the dirt, spit into them, and stepped to the plate to face Lions pitching ace Bobby Cowlick, already massaging his right arm at the sight of Frank.

"Strike the bum out!" Bobby's father yelled from the visitors dugout, and that was one of the better names being hurled at Frank from the bleachers and the visitors bench.

Faster than you could spell "Fros-T-Cream," Frank creamed Junior's first pitch over the centerfield fence.

Rounding first at a casual trot, Frank could have been excused if distracted by visions of the world's largest waffle cone swirling inside his batting-helmeted head. He no doubt was somewhat distracted from all the boos and hisses issuing from the heckling hags with megaphoning mouths in the bleachers.

By the time Frank hopped upon home plate, Old Man Cowlick was stomping toward the pitcher's mound, where Junior's arm was sagging so much you would have thought it needed a sling, but the old man did not stop there, and instead stomped all the way to second base where he wheeled around and appealed to the home plate and only umpire, who was not wearing new glasses, or for that matter, any spectacles at all; that Frank the Tank had tanked out rounding second.

The umpire promptly heaved a thumb over a shoulder, signaling the pride of the Titty Lickers had failed to tag second base.

Needless to say, the T.L. on Coach Girth Graziani's ball cap did not stand for *Tight Lipped* and he promptly expressed his world opinions and those included a few about umpiring, particularly the call he just witnessed, and his sister, who out-girthed Girth, just happened to possess a few cackling qualities herself and owned her own section of the bleachers behind home plate, added her two cents worth, compensating for the inflation rate.

Egged on by the cackling exhortations of his beloved sister, the TL head coach headed toward home plate where stood Frank bummed out from being frankly told he was not going to be licking free chocolate custard any time soon and also from being called *bum* by the gleeful Lions glee club in the centerfield bleachers, now standing upon their tiptoes either to get a better view of this free entertainment or to give the ump a standing ovation. Before you could say "Let's be good sports about this," Coach Graziani was graciously expressing his sportsmanlike opinion with a gratuitous barrage of high-fives, a few of which might have landed an inch or two below the bottom of the ump's chest protector.

By the time I had heard the third secondhand account relayed from a firsthand witness, it was Titty Lickers assistant coach Gary Humes Senior who had appealed the decision at the backstop behind home plate, appealing to the umpire's sense of fear at the point of a switchblade, and that the umpire was wearing a new set of glasses and that Old Man Cowlick actually approached Frank after the contest and said "Nice game."

About the last thing I expected after my team Cattrells had beaten Hancock Manufacturing (in T-town speak pronounced "Hand Cock") was an open palm extended toward me, an opponent saying "Nice game." But there he was—the opposing catcher, Keith McFerren, now wearing a floppy cotton madras hat and a copper chain bracelet upon the wrist of his greeting arm.

"Thanks," I said.

"You hit the hell out of the ball," Keith said before I could even think about saying "nice game" back.

"They took some funny hops," I replied. My grandfather, John Petras Sr, always used the baseball metaphor "that life sometimes took funny hops." He had played for the local semi-pro team, who once beat the barnstorming Pittsburgh Pirates.

"You beat us fair and square," Keith said. "Unlike the cheating bitches Lions Club. One thing I can't stand is a cheater."

"Me too," I said.

In all my twelve years, all of my close friendships came about because of close proximity—the same neighborhood, the same classroom, detention. We acquaintances at first tolerated one another because there was no one else available, like hand-me-downs, and we just kind of grew into friendships. But with Keith the moment I met him I just knew we were a perfect fit, tighter than two Twinkies. We were Soul Twinkies.

I invited Keith to visit my neighborhood.

On the way to the hideout my gang called *Nicotine Alley,* I told Keith about my grandfather while he told me about his family. He was pushing alongside me down Ridge Avenue his bicycle, a maroon roadster with multicolored streamers spilling from white handlebar grips, and not one but two baseball cards were clicking against the front wheel spokes.

Despite our instant twinning, we had few traits in common except that we were both going to attend S.C. Dennis Junior High after summer and we thought the Beatles were the coolest band ever, that Barbara Feldon was 99 degrees boiling hot. We shared the same feelings about girls, being once bitten and twice shit on. I was a Catholic, a Catholic school dropout; Keith was a part-time protestant and had spent all his time in public schools. I was a south-ender, Keith a north-ender. He had an older brother, Dave, whom he called *cool*. I had three sisters, whom I called *cold-hearted tattletales*. Most of all, Keith was the first kid I knew whose parents were divorced. Keith was cool with his family situation and said, "I don't mind because I get twice the presents on my birthday and Christmas." And his mom was a rare mother who worked and worked full time at Sears and Roebucks, where my dad worked selling furnaces.

Despite these differences, Keith and I clicked—clicked like two baseball cards in the same spokes. Being together could have come about only from some kind of funny ball hop.

I led Keith and his bicycle to our neighborhood smoking den, a cavity behind head-high shrubs shielding the sunny side of a concrete block garage owned by the Hughes family. Sometimes they parked a car inside their garage. I think the Jockos named this redoubt Nicotine Alley, the tar-sintered rut that ran the length of the upper block between Federal Street and Biltmore Avenue. I was fairly certain the Hughes would have said they disowned the little cubby hole we weed fiends claimed as our clubhouse, or would have said it never existed.

Behind a small copse of trees across us stood a corner grocery store, Andy's Superette, one of our main sources for cigarettes. Back then, there was no Surgeon General and no warning labels on cigarette packs. The only admonition against smoking was the unwritten, undocumented and unstudied highly popular one suggesting smoking stunted your growth. As long as you were tall enough to reach the counter, any mom and pop store would sell you cigarettes provided you told the clerk the cigs were for your mom and pop.

Our cigarette club usually kept a communal supply of smokes inside the recesses of the concrete blocks upon which we used as smoking lounge chairs. I probed inside every concrete cavity and came up with only an empty protective plastic case that kept our smokes fresh and dry and smoky.

"The Jockos must have beat us to the stash," I said, shrugging my shoulders.

"That's okay, I have some money," Keith said, fishing out a 50-cent piece from a pocket of his baseball pants.

I continued searching our lair for hidden smokes while Keith went to Andy's. I found a Zippo lighter with about enough flint and fluid remaining to emit two sparks.

Keith returned with two Crass cherry pops and a Hostess Twinkie, handed me a pop and then slid from the front of his pants where a sweaty cup protector had been an hour earlier a fresh pack of Marlboros. "Borrowed these," he said, "I'll pay them back someday."

Somehow, the lighter took a funny hop and lit on the first attempt. I lit my Marlboro with the flaming Zippo and then Keith lit his from my smoldering ember.

Over the years, I have learned that communion is much more than a ceremony the Jockos and I called *halftime* when we snuck out of Sunday mass. It is about sharing something, whether food, drink or experience, that makes us more like each other even if we had participated in the same rites before. And then, we pretend they are totally new ones.

Soon Keith was turning nearly every color of his madras hat. But he was a quick learner and on his second Marlboro he was blowing smoke rings so tight he could have worn a chain of them on his other wrist.

"I think the Marlboro Man is really cool," I said about the dude in the television advertisement, a cowboy who wore a really cool coat and was always surrounded with every smoking hot chick except Barbara Feldon.

"He's the real deal," Keith added. "No phony like the one in the Tareyton commercial. One thing I can't stand is a phony and a cheat."

"Me too," I said, clinking our cherry pops.

We sipped our cherry pop. We smoked Marlboros. We broke the Twinkie.

STEALING HOME

My first memory of playing any kind of baseball comes from the backyard of my paternal grandparents' home, a bunch of the neighborhood kids there, including the best six-year-old player, Chrissy Molchan, my first friend ever, who just swatted a Wiffle Ball over the white picket fence across the alley onto a neighbor's lawn, and now I was facing my 65-year-old grandfather, who stiffly lobs an underhand pitch toward me.

Six years later I am an all-star, at bat in practice, facing Chris Molchan on the mound, my newest best friend Keith McFerren sitting in the visitors dugout, although not on the team. I take a few warm-up swings before stepping into the batters box, cock my 30-inch Roger Maris signature bat back, shoulders level, knees slightly bent, weight on the back on my right foot, left heel an inch or so off the ground. I flex my grip on the thin bat handle, my knuckles tempered by the temper of nuns. I can feel the mid-July sun caress my upper back.

"Whoa, hold it right there, Bush!" cried all-star coach Gene Cowlick, stepping out of the home dugout toward me. I let my shoulders slump, loosened my grip, remembering old man Cowlick had been calling me Bush, short for *bush league* ever since the beginning of the season when I was playing first base and he was taking up space in the coaching box there. I had just stabbed a line drive for an unassisted double play, the official Little League Spalding ice-cream-coning in the web of my mitt. "Luckiest catch, I ever did see," old man Cowlick said to me. I might have given my opinion about his opinion and maybe his coaching.

We jawed back and forth the remainder of the game, which we won, almost no-hitting the Lions, a game in which Billy Newbold would have recorded his only gem had I not misplayed a fly ball in shallow right field, after which old man Cowlick nearly gave himself a brain hernia laughing so hard while calling me every kind of bush you could think of except *Anheuser*. I had a nagging suspicion Junior and I weren't going to become best buds any time soon.

We called him *Hygiene* behind his back—most times. A game or two I might have suggested he try washing behind his ears or trimming his nose crop and performing a couple of other rituals that would require some shoving and a whole lot of hygiene afterwards.

Standing over me, my suspicions about his hygiene habits confirmed a couple of months later, he said, "You are going to break the bat." Then Hygiene wrenched the bat out of my hands and twisted it a half turn and pushed it back into my palms. "This is the trademark," he said, tapping a hairy booger picker on the wood-burned Louisville Slugger logo. So, I gripped the bat exactly as he had instructed and prepared myself to face Chris, whose best pitch was a fat ball served right down the middle of the plate. I feasted my eyes on the ball, appearing so fat you could clog your arteries just by looking at it, as Chris released it.

I swung. There were two simultaneous cracks, the crack of the ball meeting the bat, and the one in the bat, three if you counted all those in the field collectively cracking up, including Chris, whom I hadn't seen doubled over like that since Mother Mary Paula demonstrated a grand slam on his ass.

I stared at the fault line running from the handle almost to the barrel, smug knowing it was not my fault, but Hygiene's. I was pretty certain the B.O. going on with him did not stand for *batting order* and where to place me in it.

Shrugging my shoulders, I sauntered toward the collection of bats extending from the chain-linked fence beside the dugout. One bat stood out like a sore middle finger, Junior's, hands off to even the best players on the team, like Albie Tond and Tombo Koehnlein. Junior's bat was custom made as was his glove. He also owned two pairs of cleats, one for playing the infield and the other for pitching.

Then old man Cowlick did call me *Anheuser*. "You got the attention span of the town drunk!" he screamed. "Don't think about batting for me ever again, Bush—Anheuser!" He chuckled a few moments at his latest witty insult, then regained his angry composure. "Pick up your magical glove and get the hell out of here and don't let the gate hit you on the ass on the way out!"

Well, there wasn't much chance of the gate doing that because it was rusty, hung on one hinge and swung like half of the Lions Club, who represented nearly half of the all-star team, hand-picked like Hygiene's boogers.

"And your friend is banned from this field for the rest of the year!" my ex-coach hollered as we approached the gate, which should have been dedicated to the Lions Club.

Keith heeled around and hollered back, "Bye, Hygiene!"

When I was a kid, camping out meant running around the woods all night; sleeping out meant running around town all night.

We slept out on porches, we slept out in backyards, front yards, yards that didn't belong to us, garages, ballfields, parks, dugouts, the river bank; we even on occasion or two tried to sleep upon a roof. The most important piece of equipment for sleeping out was your sleeping bag. Not only did you use it as a pretense for sleeping, you used it to transport the necessary goods to make sleeping out more pleasurable, to tote such items as cigarettes, flashlights, fireworks, pop, snacks, transistor radios, lighters, girlie mags, and more.

You could have stuffed the pouch of your sleeping bag with the complete set of your mother's good china and still would be able to roll it up as tight as the Mummy's tube socks and tote it inside the crook of your arm.

The pouches of sleeping bags always, to me, looked as though they were lined with material made from hand-me-down pajamas. Maybe that's why sleeping bags appeared to adults made more for snuggling than for smuggling.

Keith and I were sleeping out in my backyard next to the alley. We were not wearing watches; so, the only way we could estimate the time was by the number of houses going dark. Finally, the last neighborhood light flicked off its last lamp, and we sat up upon the lumpy cushion provided by our sleeping bags under the silver light of a three-quarters moon. Surrounded by nightfall, the only sounds we heard were the raspy puffs of a blast furnace across the Ohio River—slow, steady puffs as if keeping cadence of a slumbering dragon's heartbeats.

We were passing screwdriver back and forth, not the mechanical kind, rather the kind that could turn your personal screws lefty-loosey. It was a communal thing for kids sleeping out that we shared the same drinks and smokes, stories, music; reveal our ambitions and sometimes our deepest secrets to become more like the other person. We listened to Paul McCartney croon "Yesterday" on my transistor radio as silver slivered on our glass bottle. Keith and I agreed the Beatles were the greatest band ever, that "Yesterday" was their best song. We agreed screwdriver tasted like three kids of liquid shit, but we were going to drink it anyway. And we had an ambition for the night that we agreed to keep secret forever. A secret shared by only two people for a lifetime sealed a special bond between them.

Our ambition for the night was to disrupt the ambitions of our all-time enemy, wannabe coach Gene Cowlick. We would accomplish our goal by stealing every home plate and pitching rubber in T-town.

So, we slinked off into the cloak-and-rubber-dagger night, our sleeping bags slung over our shoulders like two burglar sacks while taking a clandestine route known only by someone who has spent much of his youth avoiding dudes who didn't like his looks and dudesses who did like them. I toted my official collapsible Boy Scout shovel along with a small crowbar inside my sleeping bag while Keith carried the refreshments inside his.

Our first stop was the ballfield at S.C. Dennis Junior High, where we would both attend after summer. Homeplate came up with a little digging, a little prying and a few magical words my father said while doing home repairs, and I recorded my first official sack.

43

I dedicated it to my ex-girlfriend Patty, who had dumped me for some chump already driving, buying his own cigarettes and probably carrying a fake I.D. While Keith was digging out the pitcher's mound he made a dedication to an ex named Sherry. The rubber was actually anchored with cement and much too heavy and too jagged to haul inside the delicate fabric of hand-me-down pajamas. Keith hoisted the rubber waist high, I grabbed the opposite end, and we lugged it to Sloane's cornfield where we heaved it amongst the towering stalks.

Then we stalked our way to the Little League Field in the middle of town where I dedicated its home plate to my arch-enemy, old man Cowlick, Keith doing the same for Junior because he simply did not like his looks nor his pitching cleats. The pitching rubber seemed a tad lighter than the one at S.C. We hauled it to the concession stand standing about ten feet beyond the right field fence where we shotput it upon the concrete roof, the impact making the sound of a hundred trademarks taking a dump. Instantly, dogs howled liked old man Cowlick blaming a loss on a broken bat.

We had to skedaddle in a flash.

Keith and I were sharing enemies. Keith and I were sharing labors. We were sharing a crime. We were bonding like concrete on a pitching rubber.

We grabbed our sleeping bags, mine now twice as heavy with the added stolen home plate. We slid down the dewy grass slope toward the playground side of the community swimming pool and tunneled through a u-shaped clay drainage pipe that burrowed beneath a chain-linked fence that was supposed to keep out midnight marauders like Keith and me. The dew was getting so heavy I could taste it.

We didn't reach any farther than one block down the freshly tarred alley that sloped gently between Jefferson and Trenton streets when we saw a cop car coming toward us, two search lights beaming along the neighborhood, dogs barking like the Lions Club bench at an umpire needing glasses.

"I have an idea," Keith whispered. I followed my best friend to some dog-free backyard. We slid inside our sleeping bags and pretended to snooze upon our backs, mine cushioned by two official Little League home plates and two official Boy Scout digging implements. Keith and I were sharing the same experience, the same pain and now faced the possibility of sharing the same jail cell.

We pretended to be snoring when the spotlight beamed upon our angelic mugs. We sat up stretching, yawning and rubbing our eyes. I recognized the cop as Harry Taylor, whom almost everyone in T-town called Harry the Hawk because while cleaning his official T-town Police pistol shot himself in his own foot. I was expecting him to force a confession out of us at gunpoint. Instead, he pointed the beam of his heat lamp into Keith's eyes. "Did you boys see anybody come down this way or hear anything suspicious?" Harry the Hawk asked.

"No, sir, I am a really sound sleeper," Keith said in a tone Rip Van Winkle might have used upon discovering his clothes were out of style.

The Hawk waved the beam to my face. "How about you, and don't tell me you were hibernating, too?"

I pointed up the alley, moonlit dew glistening off its freshly tarred surface. All Harry the Hawk had to do was check the soles of our shoes and it was tar and feathers for us. "I did hear a couple of garbage cans tumbling over across from the ballpark," I said.

The Hawk waved his portable heat lamp back and forth across our future mug shots. I could feel myself smirk. I had always smirked when I lied, even when someone thought I was lying when I was telling the truth. I squinted extra hard to wipe the smirk off my face.

The cop car spit gravel and shot up the alley.

In about the time it took to count all the home plates we had stolen, we were huffing it down the alley at inside-the-park-homerun speed all the way to the concrete canopy everybody in town called the Overhead Bridge, the only passage in town that prevented lengthy car traffic delays caused by trains rumbling along the railroad that bisected town. We sprinted fast enough that we would have missed tagging a few bases along the way.

Reaching the Overhead, under its shadows, we slinked with our payload along the north sidewalk, the smell of pigeon shit dominant along this passage. We then trucked up the tracks northward, ducking into the ditches that ran parallel to the rails every time we spotted some car lights beaming within our vicinity.

At long last, we reached the high school baseball field where we dedicated our crime to Harry the Hawk's foot and to his partner Beep Butler.

Both the rubber and plate were cemented; so, we had to sled them both with our sleeping bags to the left field fence where we heaved them over. Listening to the man-made boulders crashing through the brush, bounce off trees, cartwheeling and somersaulting and performing other vandal acrobatics and then splash into the river was simply a kind of entertainment you couldn't buy at the once-a-year-every-summer carnival.

In about the time it took to ride the tilt-a-whirl, I found myself for the first time at the mouth of Croxton's Run where this foothill tributary dumped into the Ohio River. Back then you could smell the Ohio River before you could see it, and when you finally could see it, you could taste it and then wished you hadn't. You couldn't have washed that aftertaste away with a bottle of screwdriver and a warsh cloth. The river smelled like decaying matter, with heavy traces of dead carp and catfish and other bottom feeders, and a strong finish of a rat's ass. You could have rated the purity of Ohio River water on a scale of one to ten, this ten being perfect for 10-30 weight viscosity. No matter where you waded in the river, one slip could lube your lungs and you would go down to Davy Jones's junkyard.

At the creek mouth, a sandbar scalloped fifty yards wide and fifty yards out. Here, Keith said you could wade out nearly that far and the water would never flow above your waist. Take one step too far and you would drop off a shelf and get pinned by the mad currents, exactly what happened to this unfortunate, poor kid named Joey Geiger, whom Keith attended sixth grade at Lincoln School. A lot of kids there made fun of Joey Geiger because of the way he dressed, where he lived and his family. Keith felt really bad that he had never took the time to get to know Joey, to chat with him.

"It isn't much, these home plates, but it's the least we can do for him, give him something to play with," Keith said. "The tricky part will be slipping them over the edge without stepping off it." He pointed to a buoy about fifty yards out. It stood out like a giant come-here finger.

Wearing our Converses, gauchies and copper chain bracelets, we stepped into the river, warm as bathwater and probably just like it on a Saturday night after an entire family of eight kids had shared it. Luckily, the near-full moon beamed a band across the rippled surface as we stepped toward the come-to-me buoy. Every minute or so, the moon would sneak behind a cloud; every time we would stand still, each of us clutching a home plate like a life jacket someone had tossed to us from a rescue boat. Every few feet forward I could feel a patch of icy currents, *ghost water* old timers in town called them, designating the spots where people had drowned. I told myself these weird caresses were merely some oil or other pollutant like Freon or solvent that had been dumped freely somewhere upstream.

The moon disappeared. Then I felt these tickle bites all over my exposed skin. I thought maybe my mind was playing tricks on me or the river rats were baiting me. Further into the harried night I waded farther into the hairy water.

The moon peeked again, this time appearing red. I could not see Keith anywhere.

"Keith," I called softly. The only sound I heard was a tug boat chugging upstream in the distance, and fading.

"Keith," I called again, this time loud enough to spook the river rats.

47

The moon continued to play peek-a-boo and still no Keith. I didn't know whether the sensation taking over my body were tickle bites or the goosebumps of fear. I felt myself trembling. The goosebumps were leapfrogging one another. I said a Hail Mary and still no Keith. I promised God if he would keep Keith from falling off the shelf and drowning I would no longer skip church at halftime. Still no Keith. The chugging faded into silence in the distance. This silence enveloped me like a cold fog. I made the sign of the cross with my thumb on my forehead. Still no sign of Keith. Then I promised God I would quit jacking off.

I heard nothing but silence.

I started crying.

Torpedoing through the surface was Keith, home-free without a home plate, laughing so hard I thought he was going to need a new ass. "Well, I know at least one person who will cry at my funeral," he said.

"Oh, no, I will not," I said, my voice as cold as ghost water. "That's a promise." And I was not smirking.

I winged my home plate at him, barely missed.

Minutes later, in the mud-veined silence, we were sitting upon a log on shore, waiting to dry off. We smoked a cigarette each and finished the screwdriver and then stole our way home.

TACK-TICS

I had survived a six-year gauntlet of nuns, my body tempered by a medley of straight-edged rulers, rubber whips and other implements and tortures banned by the Geneva Convention.

Clear back in third grade, the nuns deemed me rebellious and disruptive. They placed me in the first steps of spiritual realignment, a program by which the nuns would remove the unruly spirit within you and replace it with the Holy Spirit, as Joe Campbell was undergoing back when I was sitting at my desk in Mother Agatha's classroom. I watched him whisked inside by the crook of his elbow, clutched by the principal and Mother Superior, Mother Lucilla, another kind of mother we called her behind her back. Crimped on the bridge of Joe's freckled nose was a wad of Double Bubble, the gum a shade or two lighter than Joey's red face.

Mother Lucilla's mug was beaming as though she had just discovered a sin so rare it had eluded theologians for centuries and she was well on her way to receive a Nobel Prize. "This is what happens to you when you get caught chewing gum inside my school," she cackled loud enough to be heard over the volleys of 40 third graders laughing themselves to a new level from getting such bargain basement amusement.

Then she strong-armed Joe into the hallway, with another five stops remaining on Joe's "Farewell Forever to Bubblegum Tour."

The only discipline Mother Superior was teaching us with her mobile demonstrations was bladder control, on a quick count, our class down to six or seven cases of the pissy pants.

A few years later, I was ensconced in Mrs. McFerren's 7.6 homeroom. I wanted to fit in my new school but felt like a fish out of the water, and a bottom feeder at that, like a mudcat, or a channel cat. I wanted to be a cool cat.

Held back, Joe Campbell was also attending S.C. Dennis Junior High, presently sitting in another seventh-grade homeroom, hopefully with a fresh pack of Double Bubble.

On my first day in Mr. Smith's third period Ohio History class, trying to make a good first impression, I stood up in the aisle to answer a question and 30 other classmates laughed and pointed at me as though my dick was sticking out and chewing gum was pinched on it, 31 counting the teacher. I could feel my face turning double the shade of Double Bubble .

Standing up showing the utmost respect for a teacher or priest at St. Francis School was pumped daily into our Catholic cranial reservoirs like holy water, and if you didn't stand up as straight as a martyr tied to the stake and for a certain time limit, a nun would relegate you to the linoleum, kneeling, your nose pressed to the floor like a fly to flypaper for the remainder of the period.

After lunch, in Mr. Martin's geography class, I stood out like someone who stood to answer a question in public school. This time, my zipper was down.

I had to do something that this parochial school pariah could establish himself as cool as a rotten cucumber, something fast, pull something out of my mickey ass, like my ears, which I started wiggling. Bobby Zamborsky, whom we called Little, Jim Saner, Bob Baker and a few other boys sitting near my desk thought this display of jitterbugging ears was the funniest thing they had seen since I stood up exposing my Fruit of the Looms. Next thing I knew, Mr. Martin was pinching an ear and that ear belonged to me, and he was leading me with it to a rear corner of the classroom, repeating over and over, "I am going to hang this ear on my Christmas tree."

I remained in the corner for the remainder of the period, my nose now adding the experience of inhaling lead paint to my academic resume.

Mr. Martin was as boring as Black and Decker, drilling you one minute with the state capitols, the next 49 sandblasting you to sleep while he droned ad infinitum about his Pennsylvania farm. Come a syllable or two near *pen* and you were soon pulling turnips in his fields. His voice was as flat as his haircut, as flat as his lectures. He was so flat the only geography he probably was familiar with was that of Flat Earth.

And Carl Martin was in some kind of zone this sixth period.

Normally, we would have assumed a vegetative state, but it was Friday, the high school football team was scheduled to play at home under the lights, and we were keyed up about goofing off behind the visitors bleachers and making out with chicks at the Manos Theatre Saturday night.

There was an abnormal amount of pencil fumbling and handing off of notes going on in class. Farmer Martin would not have noticed my ears jitterbugging had they been tasseled with corn-flavored Juicyfruit he was so zoned out. That was plan B. In plan A I was aiding and abetting with other co-conspirators in what would be soon known as the Great Tack Attack.

Little did a little purloining of tacks from Mrs. McFerren's bulletin board. In fact, a marbles sack of them. When class cutie Patty Cooper left for the restroom, Little set a six pack of them upon her desk seat—points up.

While we waited for Patty to return, we conspirators pretended to be paying attention to Mr. Martin as he prattled on and on about root vegetables and pot ash and crop rotation and the price of beans and the virtues of chicken manure over cow manure and that you could use manure from rabbits and horses and goats and other bull. One more minute listening to the flat discourse of this would-be teacher and I would soon be flatlining when suddenly out of the blue stalls Patty appeared, totally unware some serious shit was about to go down. Patty was one of the prettiest girls in the entire seventh grade. She had soft light brown hair that spilled hallway down her green and black plaid dress and had a build as though she were made of T-town City bricks.

As Patty was about to sit, I was overcome with at least seven kinds of emotion that included chivalry, guilt, pleasure, impure

51

thoughts, being cool and, most of all, fitting in. She smoothed out the back of her dress and squatted down. Needless to say, Patty was not made out of T-town City bricks, nor was she wearing tack-proof panties. She rocketed out of that desk shrieking as if she were just bitten on the ass by a river rat, who happened to be in the desk behind her, clutching his belly.

Of course, everyone in the class stood up craning their necks to see whether Patty's distress would lead to further entertainment. All the commotion gave us the time to set more tacks as deftly and quickly as pin setters at the old bowling alley. Judy Gobble and a couple of other cuties, according to plan, were about to gobble up a mess of tin-coated thumbtacks by the seats of their skirts.

You would have thought after seeing Patty's plaid skirt looking like a Scottish bulletin board, the other girls would have not thrown caution to the windbag down on the farm and inspected their seats before we decorated their other kind of seats, but they were soon hopping to their feet like Catholic schoolgirls trying to answer their definition of *virgin.*

I am pretty sure Mr. Martin stirred to action about the fifth or sixth blood-curdling shriek coming from the tacked turnips and decided to go vermin hunting, helped by some girls and geeks who were squealing like pigs who had just learned the definition of *ham hocks.*

After a minute or so of death-marching down the hall, we were standing in front of Mr. Karaffa, the school principal and warden. Mr. Karaffa had chiseled angular features typical of North End Hunkies, like most of the first-and second-generation Petrases and Rocks, my paternal kin. During the 1890s, Slovaks came here to escape the oppressive rule of the Austria-Hungary Empire and also to seek employment in the ever-expanding clay works, most of which were in the north end of town as my dad's dad's dad had done. We T-town Hunkies were all connected, some more than others, as I was soon to find out. The principal was blunt, told us he would dish out a whack for every tack we placed on the seats of the uncooperative coeds. I said, "Put me down for three." Mr. Karaffa shot me a look suggesting the fourth-one's-free discount.

The Warden of Wood wasted no time lining us up across the front of his desk, with a nod of his angular chin commanded us to bend over in the full moon pose. He was as blunt as Mr. Martin was flat and with the blunt end of his paddle tried to flatten our asses.

I had been hit more, more-harder and with near perfect form by a gauntlet of nuns spanning six years, and I left with chin and spirits held high, chest puffed out as I marched into the hallway, harboring gladiator pit images of Mr. Karaffa wielding his paddle against Mother Mary Paula two-fisting straight-edged rulers. Some impure thoughts might have been invoked.

Although my three strategically placed tacks fell far short of Little's school record of nine, I strutted up the hallway back to class pretty sure I had sprouted some chest hair.

Back at Sleepy Acres, snug as a bedbug, I knew I was slowly fitting in at my new school, even if it meant hugging a desk with four other dudes cheek to cheek.

STANDOUTS

"I heard you were a standout yesterday," Keith said to me as we passed each other on our way to different morning classes. I just nodded tight-lipped and continued strolling down the hall. Yes, indeed, I did stand out, stood out like a fresh ass in Mr. Karaffa's office, not to mention my continued habit to stand when answering a question. The latter I had an answer: I simply would not answer any more questions.

I wasn't the only recent parochial school dropout. George Miller, Danny Baker, Joe Campbell and Benny Driscoll had all transferred from St. Francis to S.C. Dennis during summer. Seeing these familiar faces in the halls and upon the school grounds gave me some comfort while being surrounded within a completely unfamiliar atmosphere amongst many strangers. Not only did I take the A train to my new school on a group pass, I also learned Chuckie Darwin and his family had taken the F train to Columbus a few weeks after I had kicked his caboose at Glass Jaw.

I was pretty sure some of my old St. Francis classmates were happy to see me at our new school, especially Danny Baker. After lunch, I was moseying along the lower campus toward the basketball courts when I heard Danny yell from a sidewalk about 40 yards away, "Bobby Petras, Bobby Petras!" Danny Baker was a big-boned kid with short, dark brown hair and had a baby bear quality about him, a middle child with the impulsiveness of Goldilocks. He came long-striding toward me like a long-lost friend. Just as Danny was about to give me a happy homecoming bear hug, I spun around and he hopped upon my back.

I could feel the whole weight of the bear clan pyramiding upon my back with Goldilocks on top, and before she could utter "This pile is too fucking high," Danny slid off as if something wasn't sitting right—and that something was sitting in Danny's left nut, a yellow Dixon-Ticonderoga number 2 pencil—that I had been carrying in my back pants pocket, pointy end up, freshly sharpened.

Danny was moaning and wailing as though lead poisoning were already setting in.

Just that morning we had stood at attention along the gym floor in Mr. Smith's physical education class. Mr. Smith had brown hair with a touch of gray combed straight back, high temples and big teeth. He lectured us about hygiene, showering, jock straps and muscle pulls. He told us about straining muscles I had never heard of before, like abdominal pulls, hamstring pulls, sprained ankles and groin pulls. With a Phys Ed teacher knowing so much about pulls, I figured he would have little trouble pulling a brand new, sharpened number 2 Ticonderoga out of Danny's numb left nut.

The only thing that could have been more hilarious than Danny's standing there with a wooden look on his face and a yellow woody a couple of feet below was as if his dockers had been decorated with a few complimentary thumbtacks.

I led the way across campus to Mr. Smith's office down a small flight of steps below the gym and then into the back of the locker room while Danny hobbled like a dude with a stabbing pain in a deflated ball sack. The locker room reeked of wintergreen liniment, talcum powder and gym socks. Behind the locker room Mr. Smith sat at his desk, munching on a red apple. I escorted Danny by the crook of his arm inside the office. Seeing Danny as though William Tell could not tell the difference in fruit and his arrow had pierced Danny's Fruit-of-the-Looms, Mr. Smith set his red apple upon the desk. I could see the imprint of his teeth. Suddenly, I remembered his hygiene lecture and hoped he wouldn't see my teeth marks on the pencil wood.

"This is a first," Mr. Smith said, "How did it happen?"

While Danny was moaning and groaning as though a sharp lead pencil was filling lead inside his left nut, I was filling Mr. Smith in on all the details, giving Danny all the credit, even suggesting he might have pulled a muscle or two while the phys ed teacher nodded with a concerned look as though Danny would not be able to go out for the football team. Then he walked over to Danny and pulled out the pencil like William Tell would an arrow sticking from the wrong target.

"Drop your drawers, son," Mr. Smith said to Danny, who did so, revealing a gray graphite puncture ring.

Mr. Smith went to the medicine cabinet behind his desk and soon returned with a cotton swab and a bottle of methylate. "This may burn some," he said, dabbling the tincture upon Danny's wound.

The way Danny leaped and howled you would have thought he did pull some kind of muscle.

You just couldn't buy that kind of entertainment anywhere.

A few days later after school, Keith and I walked to my house. First, he stopped at Andy's, where he borrowed another pint of screwdriver, concealed in his *satchel,* which must have been a north end word for *gym bag.* I stopped home and got my bike and my transistor radio and permission from my mom to go to Keith's house—clear at the northernmost point in town.

Keith straddled the beam of my bike while I pedaled. The Beatles' "Yesterday" played again, Keith and I agreeing it was our favorite song.

About the time it takes to hobble a few city blocks with the pointy end of a lead pencil imbedded in your balls, we arrived at Keith's house, a small, green, one-floor house set in the back of a lot. He took me inside and introduced me to his brother Dave, who was an older version of Keith, except he stood several inches taller and was thicker boned and had stiffer and wavier hair, sported a broad forehead and a stronger jaw, the latter softened somewhat by a perpetual smirk that suggested he was learning life's secrets and they were all one long-running joke.

Their mom was working at Sears.

Keith grabbed his bicycle and we wheeled up Croxton's Run to his grandmother's house, a big, white, multi-floored structure. We parked our bikes with their kickstands and then I followed Keith down the creek where he had set traps for *muskrats,* another funny name I thought north enders called river rats. The traps were empty; so Keith led me up the hill overlooking the creek to a terrace called the *Flats* where ran this cool dirt oval for racing go-carts.

We returned to our bikes and then wheeled back to his end of the north end where Keith showed me his hangouts like Clint Buchannan's garage and an abandoned kiln at Kaul Clay, and Lincoln School, where Keith had attended sixth grade, and across the street stood the other parochial school in town, St. Josephs, where the north end Hunkies learned to speak Slovak, and down the street a block or so Keith pointed out the homes of the pretty junior high girls like Judy Gobble, future homecoming queen, whose can we had crowned in geography class with a tiara's worth of tin-coated tacks, and Linda Fidak, the latter who I was hoping would make an appearance on her front porch.

A fruit loop fad was the latest craze at school. A fruit loop was what kids called that little cloth hitch below the neck on the back of your sports shirts that you hung upon a locker hook. Girls would sneak up behind you and snatch the fruit loop off with a c'mere finger and collect them, as Linda had done one school recess with one of mine.

Keith and I kept riding in front of her house on Fifth Street. Making an appearance was a third wheel, one with a brown paper grocery sack nestled in a wire basket above the front wheel, one that was coming directly at this south end foreigner, a monstrosity of blue mobile metal pedaled by Gary Humes, son of the coach, in Tim Maple's third-hand account, who gave a home plate umpire a high five with a foreign object. Gary Humes was about my height, a bit pudgy, had lanky brown hair and bore the look of someone who was going to go through life missing second base.

57

He was glowering at me as if I were going to grow up to become a home plate umpire. I could have sworn on a stack of home plates Humes was muttering "Let's play chicken, chicken." Where I came from we called this test of nerves *bicycle jousting*. I didn't care whether his family stuffed their Christmas stockings with switchblades and brass knuckles. I wasn't backing down. Besides, Linda was holding Sir Robert's colors, even if they had been reduced to a strip of madras no bigger than a pinky ring.

From one end of the block to the other, Humes and I charged at each other—closer and closer. I could see his set chin, clinched mouth, a determined look in his brown eyes promising he was going to trample me like second base. I pedaled hard as I could. I vowed I would not turn away—never--not even at the last second. At the last second, we both turned away in the same direction. Wham!

There were two hits: Us bumping shoulders, me hitting the ground. By the time I stopped rolling I thought madras was going to be out of style. Luckily, the only thing broken was my chivalry.

"Are you okay, buddy?" Keith asked, standing over me, a look on his face saying his soul Twinkie had exceeded his shelf life. With an arm under my arm pits, Keith helped me stagger upright. My front wheel was flat, its rim bent like an umpire after being high-fived in the groin.

Humes was gawking inside the paper sack, his hands spreading it open to give him a better gawk. "I don't believe this," he said, this coming from a kid whose team logo could have well been French kisser.

Keith and I peeked into the bag—not a single egg in an entire Spahn's Dairy carton containing a dozen grade A extra-large eggs was cracked. We all shook our heads from side to side, giving a whole new meaning to shell-shocked.

The next evening, a Friday night, Tim Maple and I met Keith behind the visitors bleachers at the high school football stadium. I hadn't seen much of Tim since he started attending freshman classes at Steubenville Central Catholic High School. He had never met Keith before.

Every kid under the age of thirty hopped the eight-foot high chain-linked fence standing about 100 feet behind the visitors bleachers. The cops knew it, the school administration knew it, our parents encouraged it, and no one attempted to stop the overflow. On this evening, kids were scaling the fence like a siege on a medieval castle, gaining free access, using every available means to sneak in, except a battering ram.

No sooner were we inside, on stadium ground, shielded in the shadows below the visitors stands, Keith slipped out a still unsealed pint of screwdriver from the front of his jeans. He took a chug and extended the bottle toward me. I took my time taking the bottle, wiped its neck with the sleeve of my madras shirt, my copper bracelet rattling with the effort. While I was chugalugging the screwy tasting screwdriver, Tim said, "The coaches catch you drinking, they will never let you play football."

Tim's words, rattling inside my brain like links on a broken copper bracelet, I handed my oldest best buddy the pint. He just shook his head no, though he had no intentions to play football for any high school.

To tell you the truth, I didn't feel any different after chugging half a pint of cheap orange-flavored vodka. I only wanted an excuse to act cool and screwy in front of eighth-grade girls.

Sometime during the game, below the home team stands, Keith introduced me to this older dude from the north end named Chuck Andrews. "Chuck has a stomach like cast iron," Keith said. Chuck was wearing a blue-and black-flannel shirt and unbuttoned it. I had seen badder looking washboards on foreheads. "He can take any punch in the belly."

Chuck puffed out his stomach, doughy if you asked me, and motioned with both hands in front of it to signal "come on, do it." He had short cropped auburn hair, beneath which he bore a poker face, I supposed from the long-standing practice of suppressing

59

grimaces, but I could tell by the crinkles flanking his greenish-brown eyes, Chuck Andrews was really a card.

"Go ahead, punch him in the gut as hard as you can," Keith said.

I stared at the exposed belly of Chuck Andrews. To me it belonged on the floured wooden table at Johnny's Pizza waiting to be kneaded, not something hanging from the ceiling waiting to be knuckled.

"I don't think so," I replied.

"No, go ahead," Chuck said. "It's okay. I can take any punch."

Keith gave me the go-ahead nod while Tim gave me the I'm-glad-I-went-to-Central look.

I reared back and punched Chuck Andrews as hard as I could right in the belly button.

And he merely cracked a smile at me, a crazy, egg-eating grin.

Midway during our walk home, Tim paused to take a sip of water from the tee of the public well along the sidewalk of Fourth Street in front of the paper mill. As he bent over to sip the fresh, cold well water, I looked up at the night sky. Above the silhouette of the West Virginia hills in the east across the Ohio River rose the moon, the color of screwdriver, half-full.

MONKEY IN THE MIDDLE

Ever so slowly this new kid was gaining more and more new friends at his new school, if sitting at the lunch table with John Saxon, the school's only black male student means anything.

John Saxon was big and broad shouldered and sulky. He had a right to be; blacks were banned from swimming at the public pool except on Tuesdays. We didn't say much to each other except some small talk. John's soft voice belied his countenance.

Keith was sitting with some friends from his old school, Lincoln, and I pretended to be cool with that. After I sacked my lunch, I sauntered over to the outside basketball courts where a kickball game was going on with some eighth-grade boys. I could have tripped over my own jaw watching this left-footed kid Whitey Trifonoff clobbering the ball. Whitey was long and lean and all leg. He must have been born on the Fourth of July because every time his left foot connected with the ball the ball blasted off toward the stratosphere.

I hardly noticed a huddle of seventh graders hanging out just outside the kickball court. I knew only a few of them from Little League and also Joey Campbell, who had been cold to me ever since my good St. Francis buddy, Ronnie Paris, took Joey C. to Dizzy Land, giving the mickey a mouse and some goofy legs. Funny thing was Ronnie and my other St. Francis chums had been treating me like carp chum since my departure.

Whitey Trifonoff was putting on a kicking clinic. Another guy Charlie Ford would roll the big, white official kickball toward Whitey and Whitey would launch the white out of the ball over the asphalt onto the grassy slope beyond the fielders' heads, and they would step back farther up the slope and the next pitch Whitey would still launch the ball beyond them.

I must have drifted into the scrum of seventh graders, who were playing keep-away from this tall boy with wavy brown hair and black-rimmed glasses. Some kids called this game monkey in the middle, the object of pursuit a number two Ticonderoga pencil, an award from my recent experience that fell toward the bottom in a long line of boobie prizes, ranking right down there with plungers and used spittoons. This pencil was jouncing around the playground like a raffle ticket inside some giant dunce's hat in some kind of Reverse Calling. Whenever the tall kid closed in on one of the ten or so conspirators, they would lob it over his outstretched arms or lateraled below them. That tall, lanky boy had the stick-to-it-ness like the pencil in Danny Baker's left nut. He also had an arm-span like a gorilla's and was going after that yellow pencil as if it were the last banana in the jungle. Feeling brought down to a one-boy peer group, I was absolutely rooting for the underdog, in this case, the underape. I clapped my hands, clenched a solidarity fist, gave the go-get-it gesture.

In a snap I was left holding the short end of the stick—both of them—two number 2 Ticonderogas, one with a point, the other reduced to an eraser with some jagged splinters. If this were a Catholic school playground, both halves did not have enough lead remaining to write 100 times on a sheet of yellow blue-lined paper: "I will not destroy school property." I dropped those two nubs as though they were contaminated with some rare gymnasium ball-sack disease.

Then King Kong went ape shit on me.

Shoving my chest, he growled, "I'm gonna kick your ass," and I would have fallen except Joey Campbell was behind me shoving me back.

I couldn't have been more shocked had I sat on a spike made from electric lead. I froze. The tall dude shoved me again. "I don't take that shit from anybody." Besides me, after a quick count, I was pretty certain he just took shit from another ten dudes.

I could take a steel goal post and a brass-knuckled knee cap to the forehead as good as the next guy. What I could not take was losing. And the lads who wanted to put me permanently on the L column were growing larger and larger. "I don't feel like fighting," I said and started walking away, but he stepped in front of me and shoved me in the chest and growled, "We are going to have ourselves a tussle after school. I'll be there, waiting, outside the east door."

I learned from a few dozen or so boys the dude who wanted to take me to Glass Jaw was named Trim Tyler, who I didn't know whether stuck around after school so long that he was late for his bus or late for supper. All I knew that evening at home, pretending to take a sudden interest in academics, was that nobody was going to call me the late Bobby Petras.

No, they had plenty of other choice names to call me the next day at school: *sissy, yellow, coward, pansy, panty waist, gummy boy, punk.* They called me practically every name that showed up in the "No Show Book" except *pencil dick.*

One thing Trim Tyler was definitely not catching onto like that petty splinter of pine on the playground was what door I exited after school. I would sneak out the west door one day, the gym another, the wood shop garage door another and out the main front door another time. Outside, off the school grounds, I used every stealth tactic I had learned playing Release the Belgium, making myself skinny behind trees, sidling along the sides of houses, vaulting a fence of two, blending in with laundry hanging from clothes lines, slinking within the shade, crouching behind parked cars, sprinting across streets and alleys. I was a fast runner, too. A couple of kids like Mark King and Joey Chadwick called me *deer* I seemed so fast to them.

In the street version of RTB, I used all my skills to make my way home, just as with the woods version except no one was there inside jail to share cigarettes and girlie mags with, only three girls whom I had to call sisters—Mary Kay, Judy and Elaine, who collaborated a new literary genre in Tattle Tales.

63

I was sitting at the kitchen table doing my math homework when someone pounded upon the front door. Moments later, Mary Kay walked in and announced, "You have friends outside."

I could have yelled "yippie," jumped up and clicked my heels three times hard enough to pull a heel muscle. I had friends. Maybe Coner, Ronnie, Joe and the Jocko twins missed their old buddy. Maybe they were getting a game up of Release. Maybe Joe needed somebody to pull the old your-dick's-sticking-out routine on.

I strutted to the door.

A former St. Francis student was standing there all right, stood out as bright as the pink Double Bubble that once stuck on the bridge of his nose, Joey Campbell.

Behind him on the street, on the side of our front lawn hedges, under the soft amber glow of the street lamp overhead were the heads of five of Joey C's S.C. Dennis goons, including one Trim Tyler.

I could not have been more shocked had someone shoved an electric eel up my ass.

"Hey, Peachy, old buddy, how about hanging out with me tonight?"

"I would but I am grounded," I said, then slammed the door.

THE BELGIUM

I don't remember much about the football game, what the score was, or so much as who won. I don't recall whether we had *hopped the fence,* what we called sneaking into the Red Knights home games. All I recall were large crowds occupied both sides of the bleachers, the glare of the stadium lights, that Tim Maple and I were loitering beneath the scoreboard, the rich, damp smell of the football turf and that I was wearing white jeans.

The little else I do remember is that I must have stood out like a Belgian whose keeper had walked off for a bribe of smokes. Before you could flick your Zippo, Tim and I were surrounded by Trim Tyler and his gang of pencil dicks. I was a hand-me-down toboggan handed over to the enemy, shit-on-a-stick, shit out of luck.

To me, the game was over, there was no *ollie ollie in come free.* I was the last one in, the gummy baby.

As I was being escorted by Trim's pencil dicks, I has half-hoping, half-praying one out of five-thousand adults in attendance would notice something was amiss and come to my rescue. But as we shuffled outside the stadium farther and farther across campus their absence appeared to further and further my suspicions that adults were half-wits, who didn't know what was going on half the time, denied what they did see the other half.

Still I wished one adult could have interpreted the procession weaving through the crowd along the south end of the stadium and out into the shadows of campus as something amiss and with one measly tag release me.

I found myself facing Tyler at the southwest side of the high school, the entire world now reduced to an enveloping darkness, a street lamp spotlighting two antagonists squaring off, totally shielded from anyone loitering outside the stadium, like the cops and ticket attendants, not that they would suspect anything now.

Tyler slipped off his glasses, handed them to Joey Campbell and raised his fists.

I bull-rushed him, clipped his legs and before you could say "Release the" he was on the ground, disjointed, me on top of him. I was giving him one-twos. And soon they were adding up. My enemy rolled onto his belly, exposing his fruit loop, covering the back of his head with his arms and hands. I continued dishing out heaping helpings of pink knuckles while his shirt continued hiking its way up his back—nearly to his fruit loop.

"I can't move my arms," he cried.

I was no physics major and barely passing new math, but I wasn't crazy enough to believe a cotton permanent press sports shirt could permanently press someone's arms like a straight jacket in the local mental hospital, Cambridge.

I gave him a couple of whacks in the ribs and his reflexes must have been sharp enough to move his elbows down there and then I sized up his exposed face and gave him a couple upstairs for good measure.

"I can't move my arms," he moaned.

"Can't you see his arms are pinned?" Joey Campbell said.

As I let him up, his shirt curtained down and I was thinking its Cambridge curtains for me. We squared up again and I landed square upon him and he was back on his back and then squirmed onto his belly and I continued dishing out all the punishment and he was just covering up in the fatal fetal position. Not only was I taking Trim Tyler to Glass Jaw but also on a tour of the entire glassworks, but I could not make him make a donation to the I Give Society. I was doing all the giving and he was doing all the taking, taking way too much.

I stood up and solemnly said, "That's enough."

Tyler slowly wobbled up to his feet, his face looking like a raccoon's, with both ears bleeding.

Before I could think aloud "What the fuck just happened?" kids were pouring outside the stadium in our direction. It could have been halfway through halftime for all I knew. I had lost all sense of time. The darkness seemed to be getting darker.

Not that Tim nor I wanted to, we turned in the other direction— toward Tyler, huddled with his friends, the look on his face revealing he knew what the fuck happened and wished it had not.

I felt an arm wrap around my neck from behind and the full weight of another kid about my size and I was on my knees again. This time an eighth grader named Dick Dawkins stood over me and shouted, "You want to fight somebody, fight me!"

The funny thing was, as I stared at Dawkins, scowling, fists brandished, an arc of onlookers forming behind him, I remembered watching Tim Maple taking Dawkins's older brother to Tap Out City, probably my only friend's only fight ever. I was pretty sure I could take the younger brother in a split decision: after I started pounding his face, he would decide to split. I didn't want to fight any more. I didn't want to fight in the first place. I wanted only to split.

I stood up and resumed walking toward any escape route when another ass clown, with the courage only a toady could muster, tried to ambush me from behind except I sensed his approach and ducked, causing him to flip onto the lawn. I did not bother to look to see who he was; I kept trying to walk forward while making eye contact with no one. Tim and I had no other choice other than to lean our way through a gauntlet of my enemies. A couple of guys shoved us, saying, "come on, punks."

Then inside stepped John Saxon, and the gauntlet suddenly parted as if John were Black Moses and they, the Red Sea.

"We'll take you all on," John said, and like that the Red Sea turned yellow and receded, taking a sudden interest in the score of the football game and not on settling someone else's score.

I did not realize until many years later that John Saxon, the only black male in our school, came to my rescue because he felt the empathy only a repressed minority could feel. I can only imagine though never fully understand how John must have felt being banned from the public swimming pool six days a week and bearing the shame of hearing the rumors the pool management drained the pool after that one privileged day. I thought at the time that John was being chivalrous and Tim and I were the damned in distress. I was so damn dumb.

I don't remember much about walking the two miles home with Tim and John in the brooding silence that shadowed us, only that I was angry, hurt, ashamed, sad, frightened, confused and mostly numb, that the streets seemed darker than before. I can't remember what we talked about, if anything. Sometime along the long trek home I became aware the knees of my white jeans were caked with mud and grass stained and even in my muddled mixed-up-emotional state, I tried to devise a mental strategy to explain to my parents the black expanses cupping my kneecaps. I was pretty sure they were not going to buy that I was hanging out with a bunch of holy rollers from my new school and they considered nothing more of a good time than to spontaneously kneel in mud, point to the sky while praising Jesus.

When we reached the corner of Biltmore and Franklin, I thanked John for helping me and we exchanged goodbyes. Tim and I hiked up the hill along Biltmore while John Saxon, the only black male student in my school, continued to walk south down Franklin toward his home in Jeddo, a shanty town just outside of Toronto, Ohio, my hometown where segregation still numbly existed.

When I arrived home, I found the front door unlocked and everyone asleep. I locked the door, double-checked it and then tiptoed to bed. I slipped into the womb of my covers with my shirt and mud-caked white jeans still on. I squeezed my eyelids shut and wished I could sleep for a year or more until this shit-mare was over.

As I tossed and turned in bed, I thought that sleep put up a better fight than Trim Tyler had. I tried to relive Mr. Martin's flat voice in geography class droning about turnips and fertilizer and crop rotation and still I could not fall asleep—all because I could not suppress the feeling I was in some deep shit.

Then I was hit for the first time that night—the calling. If the calling came calling I would be off Scott-free, whatever that meant. Unfortunately for me, I had used up all my bargaining leverage that one night at the mouth of Croxton's Run when I had made promises to the Almighty to save Keith from becoming an eternal loiterer at Davy Jones's Junkyard. If the calling hit me in bed that night, I could give my parents an explanation for my dark kneecaps. The Holy Spirit picked out your wardrobe even though it consisted of the same drab, dark, scratchy, baggy cloth they wore in the VIP section in Hell. I could tell my parents the wardrobe changes started at the kneecaps and then spread across the rest of your body.

To get the calling to make a house call at 1017 Biltmore Avenue, my only option was to pray.

I prayed the rosary on my swollen knuckles. I got as far an Our Father on my thumb knuckle when in the kitchen the wall phone rang. I was pretty sure the Holy Spirit did not call collect. If he did, my father would not accept the charge.

The phone rang like a hotline to Hell.

I hoped my parents were so exhausted they would not hear it. Then I heard my parents' bedroom door squeak open around ring number 13, my dad's footsteps heavy upon the hardwood heading toward the kitchen where the wall phone hung. His hello was loud enough to raise Hell in most places. Loudest of all was the ensuing silence on his end of the phone. "Yes, I agree," he said in a confessional booth tone suggesting Father Cappelli issued him a new church record penance of Hail Marys and Our Fathers.

One father stomped so hard he could have shaken the rafters of Hell. My natural instinct was to pretend I was asleep and Dad would just go away. I actually thought if you squeezed your eyelids hard enough, you could induce sleep. I squeezed my eyes so hard you couldn't have wringed a fruit loop through them.

He slammed open the door, flashed the overhead light on while I pretended to be stretching and yawning. My old man ripped off the covers like some dude doing the old tablecloth trick with your mother's china handed down from her grandmother and probably some real silverware and a crystal goblet or two.

Suddenly exposed were exhibits A and B—the muddy kneecaps of my white jeans, and I was wearing them.

"That was Trim Tyler's dad," my dad said in a voice that was going to issue a new Petras house record for grounding. "He said that you jumped his son and yanked up his shirt so he couldn't defend himself. He's taking him to the emergency room. I agreed to pay for his clothes and the hospital bill. I am very disappointed I raised a dirty fighter."

He wheeled around toward the hallway, then pivoted back to me. "And put on some clean pajamas."

Laying on my back in my bed, in mud-free pajamas, I recalled the only real advice older boys and my uncles had told me about fist fighting was always to get in the first punch if you wanted to win. What they didn't say about the aftermath is that you should give your account of the fist fight first.

I had beaten Trim Tyler to the punch. Trim Tyler had beaten me to the punchline.

MEDITATIONS FROM A
TREEHOUSE

That weekend, being grounded seemed more like protective custody. If I had been up for parole and granted it, you would have needed a mule team of nuns and a bake sale to pry my fingers out of jail and then you would have had to drag me by my clawing feet clear to the street, this resistance pretty much summing up how I felt about returning to school Monday.

My father was the enforcer of all home punishments, such as sentencing a bar of Lifebuoy in the mouth, banishment of fun, and his specialty: 37 different ways of grounding a miscreant.

In general, he did not believe in corporal punishment, although he did dangle the threat of it like peas and carrots if you did not mind your P's and Q's. I am pretty sure the consensus of the Petras siblings would maintain we would rather have had our father plant wood on our asses than make us eat vegetables that tasted like petrified poop.

"You are not so big I can't take you over my knee," was another of Dad's stock sayings I did not take much stock in, especially when I was a Red Knight football player and later a member of the Marshall Young Thundering Herd, the same team featured in the Matthew McConaughey film *We Are Marshall*.

"Don't get too big for your britches" and "Don't go showing off" were other fruits he liked to pluck off the old wisdom tree. Like, what the hell had I had to go around showing off—my looks—the primary excuse some dudes wanted to rearrange my face like Mr. Potato Head: except in their version it was more like Mr. Mashed Potato Head.

I was Slovak, German, Irish; caught in a cultural crossfire, one side barraging me with *Hunky* and *dumb Pollack*, the other *Mickey fish eater*. I had blue eyes, light blond hair, pinkish skin and could

71

have put on a good race to become the poster boy of the Aryan Race, not the iconic look post World War II America was seeking.

I remember a couple of times watching from my Grandma Petras's kitchen window crosses burning upon a West Virginia hilltop less than a half-mile across the Ohio River. I thought it was some type of fireworks like the type set off on the ground on the Fourth except these were homemade and set off during the spring. Only some years later, did I learn the burning cross was a symbol of hate as were the epithets *Hunky, Pollack* and *Kraut,* mostly uttered at you by adults. Kids would just make fun of your last name by deliberately mispronouncing it.

I realized later when my son Robert Edward Junior was also a Red Knight athlete, my father, Robert Joseph, merely wanted his son humble, liked to keep me grounded in another way that I was experiencing that forever weekend. "Don't get the swelled head," Dad would always remind me if he thought my cap sized exceeded the cap limit he set on the words you used recounting an athletic exploit. Yep, Dad, that's exactly what I had in mind those past few weeks—no swelled head, no fat lips, no cauliflower ears. I had turned the other cheek, actually both of them, hightailing my tail home every day after school.

"Don't gloat" was my version of the swelled head a generation later I passed down to Junior, calmly, after he beat me in a game of one-on-one basketball for the first time. In my version, the one stated first, the punch with the punchline, I showed Junior how a good sport shook hands. Junior still tells a version I might have tried to have given him a swelled head by hurling the basketball at it.

Anyhoo, I ramble. I ramble as if I am trying to meditate with a monotonous hand-me-down mantra.

Anyhoo, I would learn later on my dad had been secretly boasting how his son beat up another kid who stood a half-head taller than his namesake. Maybe Dad enforced the grounding punishment because he was so adamant about the money-doesn't-grow-on-trees theory that he didn't want his only son going around beating up kids and being held responsible for hospital costs and reparations.

Anyhoo, he still ground me, indefinitely.

Anyhoo, whenever he went to work selling gas furnaces at Sears and Roebuck, as he did that Saturday morning, Mom let me go outside as long as the neighbors wouldn't see me, people who I believed belonged to the same Tattle Tale Network my three sisters did.

Born Pearl Elmina Seymore, my mother was of Irish, Scottish and German descent. Her red hair, emerald green eyes and airy singing voice favored her Irish heritage. She and her older sister Evelyn resided with their parents William and Mary Angus Seymore in the little town of Gallitzin, Pennsylvania in the Johnstown area, known for the second most famous flood in history.

The story passed along the back rooms of family gatherings was my grandfather caught some guy trying to play good neighbor Sam with my grandmother and beat him to within an inch of his life but wasn't sure what side of life's property line that inch sat. So, after proving he could pack a punch with an expiration date, my grandfather packed his young family's suitcases and fled to Steubenville, Ohio where he legally changed their last name to that of his mother's, McCloskey, and he then took up the great Irish-American tradition of becoming a cop.

When my family said that I took after my grandfather, I had always thought they meant *looks*, all of which explains the soft spot in her heart my mother always had for my unruly behavior because aiding and abetting ran in her family, at least in one case, to another state.

I like to think after all these years being called *Pedro, Peaches, Peterless* and any other peejorative you can think of that the patriarch of the Seymore clan had the foresight and the foreskin to nip the name-calling in the butt and pulled the old name switcheroo.

I can only imagine the verbal barbs thrown at *Seymore,* especially anytime you got near bleachers or some restroom stalls. Guys would poke more fun at that one than a Swiss surname.

Anyhoo, I slinked off under the mid-October sun into the autumn-hued woods behind the Bloomer's house across the street and sneaked away to my treehouse, which wasn't much of a structure, really, just a few wooden planks amateurishly anchored into a trunk of a hickory tree with enough air below me to qualify as a tree house, in my book, which it is.

Anyhoo, the tattle tale delegation of the Biltmore Petrases went off to play with some losers they called friends. Dad was trying to do his part in putting coal furnaces out of business; and Mom probably wanted some peace and quiet and I was quietly and peacefully puffing on my third and last Tareyton, ironically whose much advertised motto was "I would rather fight than quit."

Anyhoo, for the first time since the Golden Pencil of Discord had fallen into my hands, I felt a reprieve, peace. During my youth, actors who pretended to be doctors would broadcast on television ads how smoking a Winston or a Parliament would relax you almost to a Shrangri-la state of tranquility, unlike that experienced by the black-eyed patrons of Tareytons.

The tree house overlooked a gulley in which a creek trickled along stepping stones and spilled into a small fern-lined pool formed from a dam I had constructed with sandstones. My tree house could have served as a platform from which to take a dive into a galvanized tub-sized body of water below. My wandering mind wondered whether I should have taken a dive the previous night. I would have had to live with the shame and derision of losing, complemented with the anti-compliments of *loser, punk and pussy* instead of being dubbed *cheater, punk and pussy.* I was stuck between a rock right and a hard left.

An idea hit me like a ton of sandstone: I could take a dive, all right, cannonball right off my treehouse into the pool below bolding not much more water than your everyday piss pot. With any luck, I would only break a leg or two, enough to keep me out of school until summer break. Then I thought I would get my mother in trouble and Dad would probably banish me from any form of diving platforms indefinitely the way he did me from the kiddie pool for dunking my sister, Mary Kay, in six inches of garden hose water.

Anyhoo, sitting in the tree house, my mud-free legs dangling over the planks, my last smoke going up in smoke rings, I remembered the first time I had inhaled. Near the outhouses in the upper tract of the city park, a couple of older hoods gave us the option of inhaling our cigarettes or sporting pairs of matching black eyes, and we weren't even carrying Tareytons—the Jocko twins, Ronnie Paris and me. You might have said that we choked under pressure or as Tim Maple often said, "It was enough to gag a maggot," reminding me how affectionately the Jocko twins would call each other *maggot face.* I am pretty sure with all the color gone from our mugs, calling us *maggot face* would have been a compliment.

Anyhoo, Ronnie, Bobby, Mike and I would go on blowing smoke rings longer than any of the other boys from the upper west corner of the middle of the south end. Experts would probably attribute our habit to the artless art of inhaling. I like to think my habit manifested manfully from the sweet oblivion of forgetfulness that morning, the result of a medicating meditation upon my treehouse.

Anyhoo, for the first time I felt like myself: I could think clearly, my thoughts not clouded by survival instincts. I felt double-ought good, and I inhaled my surroundings. Whether by a trick of the eyes, a trick of the imagination, or ripples of consciousness from some transcendent source, a fuzzy halo appeared upon the mirrored surface of the water below, a golden halo wreathed within the gilded crown of the hickory. I could see that my head was blocking the sun, only its corona ringing gold around my blond hair—a mane—and my older, future, fierce, blue-eyed self was staring back at me, framed inside that golden mane, that of a lion, a lion in waiting.

75

Anyhow, I knew I was going to grow up sometime soon.

JAIL

Over the weekend, a bucket brigade of mouths had formed stretching all the way from the battle arena of the high school lawn two and a half miles south to the hallowed halls of S.C. Dennis Junior High, with the caboose slinging a full bucket of manure-mix and mud all over my already muddy reputation.

Going to classes in the halls, Monday morning, boys were going out of their ways to call me *dirty fighter, cheap shot artist*, and when they couldn't think of any insult that was in vogue, they uttered the old go-to *punk*. Some girls gave me dirty looks and nothing close to the ones associated with the impure thoughts that give them a penance of few quick memorized prayers.

I did not have a Hail Mary of a chance to score a compliment that morning as I had soon learned mud was thicker than water and was snowballing by a T-town minute and that you couldn't have doused it with all the Clorox in town, as my mom had tried with my white jeans. My reputation was as sullied as my pants.

I started to turn into Mrs. McFerren's math class when Keith sucker-punched me with a verbal uppercut to the gut. He practically shoved me in the chest with his green eyes. "I heard you are a dirty fighter. You didn't give Trim a fair chance to fight back. At least I could still respect you after he kicked your ass in a fair fight. Fuck you. I can't believe I ever called you my best friend!"

His words went down about as smoothly as half a half-pint of screwdriver. I could not have been more shocked had somebody snuck up behind me and gave me an electric wedgie.

Sitting upon my desk seat in math class, I felt unsettled, squirmy. Mrs. McFerren was demonstrating common denominators upon the blackboard when the school secretary peeked inside the doorway. Not for a fraction of a minute did I doubt what topic they were discussing.

I soon found myself two rooms down the hall inside Mr. Karaffa's office. From my experience in the principal's office, you are not invited to take a seat. If anyone takes a seat, it is the principal and you are wearing it. I stood before Mr. Karaffa from across his desk. A picture of President Lyndon Johnson was mounted upon the wall behind him between the flags of the United States and Ohio. Otherwise the room was pretty much spartan, absent of any showy trinkets, knickknacks, bowling trophies, Nice Guy of the Year citations, the only showcased object the wooden paddle leaning in a corner.

Rumor was this paddle was made of coffin wood handcrafted from a tree grown only from the Dead Sea Region and even if so much as a splinter was dedicated to you, both hemispheres of your ass were dead meat. I was surprised when I first saw this implement a month or so before that it was not ornamented with some cannibal tribe bones and feathers or painted in our school colors—red and white. It was just a chunk of bare wood with a two-fisted handle.

Some called it nun wood and none other than the Prince of Principals would wield it. In principle, I would usually say something smart about such a magnificent implement of discipline, like "You are holding the handle wrong and you'll crack the trademark," but I had a sneaky idea of what was soon going to be cracking. And the Dean of Dark Discipline had a look on his face guaranteeing I was going to remember this lesson for more than fifty years.

Mr. Karaffa leaned across his desk, gripped the edge nearest me, leaned a little farther stretching his neck out his pressed white collar like a turtle and said, "I heard reports you were involved in a fight upon school property."

"It wasn't here," I replied.

"The fight took place upon the high school campus and that is Toronto School District property."

He had me on a technicality, similar to the way nuns called the shit house *lavatory*. I knew I was in deep doodoo when I first entered

78

that office and no matter what I said or was going to say was going to matter. I had only one witness on my side, Timmy Maple, sitting or sleeping peacefully eight miles down the road as a freshman at Steubenville Catholic Central High. My only other possible witness was John Saxon and this wasn't Tuesday.

"Several witnesses, including Joey Campbell stated you jumped Trim Tyler from behind, yanked up his shirt like a straight jacket and beat him up so bad his father had to take him to the hospital."

"That's a lie!"

"Don't you raise your voice to me," he replied through clinched teeth.

Knowing what was soon coming, I didn't care a splinter's worth of coffin wood. I was going to get an assful but he was going to get an earful. Standing across this doughy, turtle-jowled, middle-aged guy wearing a suit and tie and spit-polished shoes, I thought about pulling a Stanley Chesney and flee clear to the nearest church. Then I concluded that act would only cement my reputation as a coward.

I decided to give Mr. Karaffa my side of the story and he gave me his, which was my backside.

As the principal fondled the handle of the paddle, I bent over to grasp the edges of the flat gray desk. I braced myself, stiff, my body a roadblock. I pretended I was sitting in my treehouse looking down at the reflection of my older self. I looked myself in the eyes, steel blue on steel blue, stilled my breaths, set my chin. My older self nodded, ever so slowly. Twelve times.

Then the zinging ringing stinging stopped. I stood up straight, suppressed all pain, just like Chuck Andrews practiced taking a punch to the gut. I held my poker face even if I wanted to poke right back. The principal was sweating and panting, like a paramedic.

"I don't ever want to see you in here again," he said.

Only a dumbass wanting a numb ass would want to once again position himself in the old rump roast pose for another wallop of wood but, of course, I would.

The school bell clanged, signaling the time had come to change classes. He nodded in the direction of the hall. I filed into the hallway with the other students pouring from their previous classrooms. I was hoping the weather was warm enough to still play flag football. I was on my way to attend Mr. Smith's gym class.

The following morning, Tuesday, word in the halls must have gotten out that I could not only dish out punishment I could take it; I was no glass ass. The period following my visit to the principal's office, I took my ass and the rest of my body to Mr. Smith's physical education class in which I scored three touchdowns playing flag football.

As I was about to turn into geography class, a seventh-grade boy approached me, actually grinning—Brad Engle, lead singer and guitarist for a garage band called the Brute Angels, musically, to be blunt, just brutal. "What are you doing by picking on such a little guy?" Brad asked, his speaking voice several times more pleasant than his singing one.

"Well, err, I err," I mumbled.

Brad clapped me on a shoulder. "The bigger they come, the harder they fall."

A moment of so later, Bobby Cowlick accosted me and pumped my hand. "You can play on my team any day of the week," he said. "You do what it takes to win."

Across the hall Albie Tond called me *Cassius* while making boxing gesticulations as did Craig Rock and a couple of boys whose names I did not know yet.

I could not have been more surprised at the turn of events had Joe Sokol's dick been sticking out and it was stuck in some girl's bowling ball.

Sitting inside Mr. Martin's geography class, I decided the world wasn't so much flat or so much round as it was two-sided. You had either communism or capitalism, you were a democrat or a republican, a bad guy or a good guy, and everything else could be viewed in terms of white and black, even if you could see clearly for only one day of the week.

HOME

Home, for the past few weeks had meant confinement, prison, witness protection program, self-imposed exile. In baseball, both the visiting and home teams battle over the possession of an odd-shaped plate called home upon which plenty of mustard and cheese are served but no cheese dogs. In the children's game of catchers, a tree, a square or a crack of a sidewalk or any other landmark is designated as *home,* a sacrosanct refuge off limits to a would-be catcher. Step one measly pace off home, however, and you could instantly become *It.*

In many versions of Release the Belgium, *home* is a designated area such as a clump of bushes, a copse of trees, a recess in a hillside or a makeshift cabin into which a team can sustain inviolable refuge from the marauding enemy. Neither a nun nor the big bad wolf wearing a habit and wielding a fistful of pagan baby money while saying "open sesame" could pry you from the designated *home.*

So, it should come as no shock the home room in junior high served as such a haven and over time students who met daily in this haven before school and later escorted one another to such classes as Ohio History, Geography, Study Hall, English, Mathematics, Art, Music and Wood Shoop would develop a camaraderie akin to being teammates. Shared antics made such a team tighter than two tuba players and no two-dude team had sealed such a bond than Bobby Zamborsky and I.

Bobby originally resided at the extreme north end of town and sometime early in the school year his family moved upon the hill overlooking the south end, a lane called Fairview Heights, a designation I would occasionally visit after hiking through the woods up the mountain separating that Bobby's house from this Bobby's house.

Up there, we would hike a little bit more to my Uncle John Rock's farm pond and catch bluegills and catfish. We called each

82

other *catfish* for life. Bobby Zamborsky had dark-brown spiked hair, black-framed glasses, a boxy frame. Most kids called Bobby *Little*, well because frankly he was little and also because he was always in a little bit of trouble and bore the grin to back them up. Sometimes kids and adults alike called him Zambo.

Little was the mastermind and chief tactician in the Great Tack Attack and unofficially held the stinky distinction of possessing the school record of consecutive butt-whacks until a few weeks later I learned first-ass it was far better to give than receive. Bobby and I were both Hunkies.

Our Health Class teacher, Rudy Yasich, repeatedly called Little and me clowns, adding "we would do no better than digging ditches and thumbing rides for the rest of our lives." Maybe we two Bobbies did ditch academics upon occasion and thumbed our noses at homework a couple or more times when fun was distracting us as we did in seventh grade in Miss O'Neill's library study hall when we should have been feigning interest in *War and Peas* and other literary big boys.

Little and I might have been clowning around a little too much for Miss O'Neill's liking. To me, Miss O'Neill looked like a bigger version of the Big Ethel character in "Archie Comics". I called her *Big Big Ethel* behind her back. I wouldn't have called her *Big Big Ethel* to her face even with the backup of an armor-plated support group.

Before you could say "Big and Little," Big Big Ethel was towering over us, but we continued laughing. "Stand up," she said, her voice a deep whirring rumble like that of a lawnmower. I had a slight suspicion that someone's ass was grass. We did not stir. Again, she barked, "I said sit down!"

The other Bobby gave her a look that you could interpret "as go ahead I double-dog dare you." She grabbed that Bobby by the shoulders and planted his ass to the linoleum. Then Miss O'Neill sidled over to me and gave me a commanding look. I squatted on my haunches as if this Bobby's middle name was Fido.

From that moment, I pretty much understood why librarians keep a rack of rolled-up newspapers ready.

Little by little, Zambo was becoming my best bud at school. When Keith and I passed each other in the halls or upon the school grounds, we would give each other acknowledging ""you exist" nods and a few grunts, eventually accosting each other with "how's it going?" though never apologizing for our falling out over the Trim Tyler tussle.

Well, things were not going all that well for two self-proclaimed cool catfish in Mr. Gerald Haught's industrial arts class. For some reason, Bobby and I would not fork up our shop fees. I still am uncertain the reason I didn't dish out my shop money. Maybe I didn't want to hear my father lecture about the unfruitfulness trees had bearing money, or maybe I was suspicious of anything constructed of wood, like baseball bats and paddles, and maybe because my circle of trusted grownups was tightening like a noose and I was at the end of the hemp with them.

Mr. Haught banished us to a back room no larger than an aquarium tank sitting on your averaged-sized unrepaired stereo cabinet.

Every so often, a classmate or two who had spooned over their ten-dollar shop fee to make a shoe shine stool would press his nose against the glass door window of our closet and rap upon it as if to the get attention of guppies to tell them it was feeding time.

Of course, we two cool catfish took advantage of a few folding chairs, a couple of hand drills and some bluing stain and undertook a short hobby of redesigning furniture.

Mr. Haught always wore baggy suits the color of a paper grocery bag, exactly matching the shade of his hair, eyes and tar-and-nicotine fingers. He reeked of stale Camels and sawdust. A cloud of smoke seemed to wreath his head like Christmas flock. If you saw him anywhere else at Christmas time, you would have sang, "Deck the halls with boughs of tobacco."

Sometime during our third week of confinement to the fish tank, Little had to piss like Sea Biscuit and expressed this need to Mr. Haught. Now, the only thing more stained than the shoe shine stools of which Little and I were a little short of cash paying were Mr. Haught's nicotine fingers and he flashed them in the direction of the fish tank with a resounding "No!"

Relieved of Plan A, Bobby had to resort to Plan P and promptly relieved himself by taking a capital pee in our confined cubby hole.

The water closet conversion occurred on a Friday. When we returned the following Monday for another 60 minutes of unpadded confinement, Mr. Haught told us to go to Miss O'Neill's library, shaking his head from side to side while repeating in his gruff smokers voice, "I don't know how cats are getting inside the storage closet and urinating in it" as Bobby and I struggled to stifle grins like two Cheshire catfish. I wanted to tell Mr. Haught, "I don't know anything about cats pissing, but I do know a little about one catfish puddle."

Somewhere between our exile from shop class and Miss O'Neill's, we decided to cough up our shop fees.

"School's out, school's out, teacher let the bulls out. No more teachers, no more books, no more teachers' dirty looks"—was a ditty we students used to sing the moment we stampeded through the school's exits for a vacation or an extended holiday, such as the Thanksgiving my seventh-grade year. It's curious fifty-plus years later, I can remember something as silly and insignificant as that ditty, most likely a result that something that trivial is wired and rewired into one's memory from significant repetition.

Then there are those moments that will forever weigh heavy upon your psyche, ones that replay over and over again, and you recall in the minutest detail the moments when you first learned about the abrupt pivot in history, often yours, such as the assassination of JFK; the pivots in your own history no less insignificant. Perhaps this type of permanent wiring results from replaying events again and again in your mind, wishing they never happened.

I remember exactly where I was that Thanksgiving eve: sitting in the living room with my family, watching *the Beverly Hillbillies* in black and white, when the wall phone in the kitchen rang. My mother answered it. "The call is for you, Bobby."

My homeroom classmate Bob Baker was on the other end of the line several blocks away. The moment he said "hello" I knew he had been crying.

"Keith McFerren was hit by a car," Bob struggled to say. "He was riding his bicycle home carrying a turkey from his grandmother's house when a car ran off the road and hit him. He's dead."

I remember dropping the phone by my hip, it dangling there, limply, like someone disbelieving he had just squeezed the trigger and the ensuing static numbness that overwhelmed me and consumed me the remainder of the evening all the way to my bed, the very same bed whose womb I had sought refuge a little more than a month earlier, wishing another nightmare would vanish if I just squeezed my eyes and went to sleep.

As I rolled around and around, the Beatle's "Yesterday "rolled around and around inside my head; and when I awakened in the morning I realized that that yesterday was here to stay.

A day or two later, my father and I went to the showing at Clark's Funeral Home. Keith was laid out in a casket, looking no worse than when we stole every home plate and pitching rubber in town, except he was wearing a blue suit and tie when he should have been wearing madras, especially his floppy hat. Seeing Keith like that, I broke down, breaking the second promise I made on that night that seemed like only yesterday. What broke me up the most was that I never got the chance to say goodbye.

"You must be Bobby," Keith's mom, said hugging me. "I finally get the chance to meet you."

Keith's mom looked elfish. She should have been wearing forest green, autumnal gold or anything plaid, not black.

"I am so sorry under these circumstances," my dad said.

"I have heard some many good things about you. Keith thought the world of you."

Before Dad and I left, I bent over Keith and whispered, "Goodbye." I hoped Keith somehow heard me.

CASTS

The largest bucket brigade of tales is called oral history.

When I was a boy, we boys lived under a code of ethics, mostly unwritten but relayed through generations of big mouth bucket brigades that constituted our constitutions that we lived by, and if you did not adhere to this oral history, your next one could well be a bloody mouth, especially concerning the codes pertaining to fair fist fights.

There were three unwritten juvenile laws strictly prohibiting duking a dude's lights out, most likely issued when dudes were still issuing their dukes under candlelight: One—Never pick a fight with a kid wearing glasses; Two—Never pick a fight with a kid wearing his Sunday clothes, unless he wore them on Monday or any other weekday. Three—Never tussle with a kid wearing a cast. I was wearing a cast. A mummy's worth of plaster spiraled from the bottom of my left ankle to the top of my left thigh, a result of a growth spurt that left a calcium deposit below my kneecap the size of a cabbage roll--baba-sized and just as tender-- rendering me unfit to undergo any taxing physical activities like fisticuffs. Enveloped with plaster, you could have worn your Sunday clothes to the Friday night fights and called everybody every name in the unabridged *Encyclopedia of Insults*—and added you did not like their looks or said that you could take them, and not one antagonistic cuticle could be raised to harm you.

Hell, even the backs of your britches were off limits to Mr. Karaffa. I am not sure about nuns. They would pray for guidance to the patron saint of creativity—St. Francis Assisi--and I am pretty sure he would inspire something appropriate for an incapacitated hoodlum. You could be cocooned in so much plaster you couldn't stand up to answer a question, and Mother Lucilla would make you write on the blackboard, "I will show respect to my teachers at all times," 100 times with a stub of chalk pinched between your lips, and she would write a note on your body cast reminding her to break out the ruler the moment you broke free of your plaster of Paris shell.

I was wearing my Sunday pants, the only trousers baggy enough to fit over my cast, and I was pretty much wearing them every day of the week and twice on Sundays.

Anyhow, after sunset, me and my shadow and my cast were hobbling along the playground at Franklin Elementary School, a couple of blocks down the alley from my house. I was hanging out with some of the cast from the night I sullied my white jeans and my reputation—Trim Tyler and Joey Campbell—along with seventh-grade classmates Mark King, Craig Rock, Gary Driscoll, whom everyone called Bennie or Beeban, and Donnie McFall, nicknamed Muggsy after his grandfather and uncle.

And we were all hitting it off—not the schoolground way. Maybe I had long ago said a prayer to St. Francis the Sissy, one seeking a creative answer for some school assignment I had failed to answer, a solution as original as the time Joe Sokol explained to Bennie and me the sudden disappearance of a full pack of Marlboros stowed in Joe's underwear drawer, further hidden in the piss pouch of a pair of BVDs jockeys Joe said that his brother Mike suddenly wore, with the Marlboros still tucked inside them. I thought maybe, just maybe, the Patron Saint of Creativity was just getting around to answering me, a delay for not bribing him with lighting some votive candles or sacrificing some pleasurable act when perusing girlie magazines.

Out of a night sky as black as the inside of Satan's Christmas stocking came the creative answer that had eluded me since the middle of fourth grade. My idea was to borrow some clothes line and some garbage can lids. Garbage cans were made from real galvanized steel back then, American made, union made, locally manufactured at Weirton and Wheeling Steel corporations, more durable than a petrified leg cast, loud as cathedral bells, unlike these plastic excuses of garbage cans of today, of which a single lid of these cheap sweat-shop, below-minimum-wage imports would not make a single Belgium worth capturing or bribing for.

My gift from the saint was to tie the steel garbage can lids onto car bumpers. Bumpers back then were made from real chrome-plated steel assembled in the assembly line of the United Auto Workers in Detroit, their product so shiny you and your chums could assemble behind them, dabbing your hair with Brylcreem while you bumper-skied a country mile in the city.

Together we stole our way up the alley behind school, where I stood as an innocent lookout while Trim, Mark, Bennie, Craig and Muggsy took turns as borrowers; then we stole our way back to the school grounds and then crossed Federal Street and with our borrowed goods stole down to the corner where sat Johnny's Pizza.

I could see through the picture window of the parlor Johnny tossing a disc of dough about the size of your average union-made garbage can lid. Like nonunion Thorax the Magician working the handsaw on a voluptuous assistant laid out in a black rectangular box, Johnny would work his pizza-cutter magic on the freshly baked crust and transform the once oval mass of dough into 24 cheese-sequined, equally divided, square slices with four perfect 90-degree corners, although some came out the size of a baseball card and tasted like Mickey Mantle's shoe tongues. Then Johnny would adorn these square slices of pie with a token topping of pepperonis or anchovies, the only toppings of the only pizza parlor in T-town City back then.

A few cars were parked in front of Johnny's, their drivers inside queued in front of the vinyl-topped counter. I could see their backs in front of Johnny kneading dough while off to the side some high school kid folded pizza boxes. Outside, three rear bumpers stood out like three puckered lips awaiting to be kissed for the first time.

How sweet it was the five of us lovingly tied three garbage can lids to three car bumpers. We tucked the lids beneath the chassis of each car and then stole across the street under the shadows of Smitty's Corner to watch the rotten fruit of our labor.

I dedicated the first lid to Saint Francis, although quietly to myself, promising him that if my art proved to be a masterpiece I would give him his cut the next time I won a raffle.

Before you could say "give me four slices with extra anchovies," if you could even consider mouthing something so repugnant, the first car backed out of the lot and was dragging silver sparks. The car went down Franklin as though Roman Candle was the newest model to roll off the Ford Factory assembly line and continued about three blocks before the proud new owner decided there was a major flaw in a major-sized muffler. He coasted the lemon to a stop and hopped outside. The duped dude held the lid overhead, a pose of Atlas holding aloft flat earth, then slammed it to the flat asphalt, answering the age-old question: What is the sound of one cymbal clapping? When the steel thunder finally wobbled to a stop, he started cussing and then called us every bad name you could think of except *pizza face.*

As the duped dude pulled away, spark free, we were slapping knees and laughing so hard you would have thought we were going to be next standing in line, this time at a hospital for much needed ass transplants.

The second act of this prime-time school night comedy seemed to take a tray of time--24 slices of Johnny's ticked off the pizza clock--until a guy toting two boxes was soon hauling a tail of sparks up Federal as long as a comet's, a celestial object clanging the pavement loud enough to break the sound barrier. The guy must have been really hungry because he didn't even stop to rename Haley's Comet or dragging a beat-up rusty muffler was a regular occurrence for him.

The next customer must have ordered only a couple of regular pizzas, adorned with the token sprinkles of cheese and pepperonis. He slid into his car and turned onto Federal. The sparks didn't fly for more than 40 feet when the car came to a stop and I could see by the look on the face of my Physical Education teacher the dragging steel sparks suddenly sparked an interest in garbage can forensics.

91

Mr. Smith vaulted out his car and stomped toward his back bumper, where he stooped to examine Exhibit A as if he were Harry the Hawk finding a new piece of evidence in the still unsolved crime of the Case of the Stolen Home Plates. Coach Smith undid the knot of our rig as deftly and quickly he would on an ankle wrap and held up the lid and gave it a look over as though it were some kind of booby prize for being selected last the most times when choosing sides in gym class, and about the time it takes a team captain to chant "eenie meenie minnie moe," the Phys Ed teacher was inside his car cruising up and down the streets trying to catch us by the toe or any other body parts and, of course, from toe to the tippy tops of our toboggans we were cast within night shadow watching our favorite teacher partaking in our new favorite source of entertainment: shaking a fist outside his car window, yelling, "I know who you are and you are in big trouble!"

Of course, he had no more an idea about who we were than we would on a pop quiz in his Ohio History class the next day. The only way Coach Smith was going to blow the lid off our cover was if we laughed so hard we would pull our abdominal muscles.

Later on, watching one final garbage can lid jouncing along the ruts and rocks topping the alley behind Franklin School, I became aware again that events in life sometimes took some funny hops, like Trim Tyler and I were now friends. Maybe everything, no matter how grand or insignificant they seemed at the time, were all connected, that life was merely a continuous play and we its players; and all those funny hops are our cues, our cues to play the roles no one other than ourselves can perform.

I said goodbye to the cast in this act and exited up the alley.

Like my life thus far, my stride seemed like one funny hop after another and I didn't know where they were leading, only that they were leading me somewhere, that I would know when I arrived. As I crossed Madison Avenue and continued up the shadowed alley, my leg cocooned with twenty pounds of plaster, a sliver of the moon appeared, no more than a spark really. I hobbled home, one gimpy step at a time, into the hobo night.

RELEASE

Release is the ultimate team sport. To capture the bad guys' flag-substitute while protecting yours—whether it be a toboggan, some kid's T-shirt or a borrowed garbage can lid—requires from every teammate, whether five or twenty, cooperation, strategy, stealth, diversion, sacrifice, discipline and an occasional communal smoke or two. All players know their roles and any deviance or disloyalty could result in the neighborhood humiliation of defeat, that is until the next day and a new contest is staged, or the continuation of a never-ending-all-summer one.

I like to think my participation in Release from an early age on the meanie streets of the Upper West Corner of the South End and its forever-green, free-for-all, wrap-around woods inculcated within me the spirit and harmony and values one can obtain only from repetitive practice of teamwork.

I was a junior, a starting defensive end for the Toronto Red Knights, coming off my best three games ever, and playing against our bitter rival, the Jefferson Union Yellow Jackets. It was homecoming.

To tell you in a synopsis of this longstanding rivalry, the fans from J.U. called us *river rats* we called them *clod hoppers, cow paddies* and every pejorative ever associated with the Four H Club.

The week leading up to this huge encounter, I would mentally prepare myself with hours of meditating in a secluded spot chanting the mantra "P.U.J.U."

The tone was set for the evening when during pregame ceremonies some J.U. juvenile delinquents (J.U. J.Ds) dragged a bloody dead chicken around Red Knight Stadium, witnessed by full bleachers of fans on both sides and another crowd packed along the fence beyond the south end zone. Of course, we homestanding Red Knights were oblivious of the foul fowl play going on along the perimeters of our much-cherished field because inside our castle-

94

turreted locker room, coaches Ralph Anastasia and Paul Kaliivoda were trumpeting pep talks, their topics basically consisting of "They hate us; we hate them; and we could lose nine games this season and only beat J.U. the season would be a success." Our coaches didn't have anything good to say about J.U. except that they had good tuba players and their cheerleaders took first place at the State Fair, as livestock, and their boys had some basic math skills and called counting sheep *erotic dreams.*

We would learn the choked chicken turned out to be no more than a rubber duck dabbed with Heinz packet ketchup. But the homestanding Red Knight fans remained aghast by the heinous deed committed by the barbaric visitors.

Despite motivated by a hatred usually reserved for minorities, we came out on the short end of the yard sticks, trailing by eight points with nine seconds remaining, P.U.J.U. in possession and no time outs remaining for us, though we never lost our fighting spirit, at least I thought so inside the huddle. I remember hunkered over the defensive huddle with Frank Slowikowski, J.R. Pope, Joe Obertance, Louis Dukes, Albie Tond, Larry Hughes and Howard Mosti, somebody distinctly growling through his facemask: "We might lose the game, but we are going to win the fight. Everybody come out swinging!"

I came out swinging. Imagine my surprise when I learned I was the only one of eleven teammates to come out swinging. Imagine my surprise when I came out swinging on the largest player on J.U. and found myself suddenly sprawled upon my back. Imagine my surprise to learn the referees had called time out with one second remaining in order to eject me from the game. And imagine my surprise when assistant coach Frank Wilson came up to me after that one tick had expired and said, "That was the most selfish act I have ever witnessed on a football field."

Picture twenty-some years later I am sitting upon the home side bleachers with my wife Debbie, watching our sophomore son play defensive back for the Red Knights. Jefferson Union has long been

95

defunct, but the loathing has been projected upon Steubenville Catholic Central.

My former teammate and co-captain Bob Morris and one of the ten on-field teammates who watched me go down swinging is now the head coach of my son's team.

The present version of the Red Knights hate mantra was "Fuck Central." And they chanted "Fuck Central" breaking out of every huddle even when they weren't playing Central or football.

A bizarre alphabet soup rolled around full circle inside my head: "P.U.J.U.F.U" while watching the Red Knights below on the same field I had played. It was the fourth quarter of their tenth game, the Knights' record two wins, seven losses. I was still stewing that my son is not the starting quarterback. I was still stewing I was the only one who came out swinging 20 years before. In small high school sports, only three different perspectives count. I had learned at one time or another seeing from all three—that coaches hate to be proved wrong, that sportswriters hate to be proved wrong, that parents refused to be wrong. And this parent was doubling down on his triple-sighted view.

The Red Knights had the ball on their own 20 and were led by Charlie Humes, yes, from the very same Humes family mentioned previously, this one third generation, who had supplanted Bobby to second team quarterback. Charlie, sometimes affectionately called Chuck, was a nice guy, wouldn't have known a switchblade from a switcheroo, athletic looking with wide white wristbands, sleek and a Senior and the ace pitcher on a very successful baseball team. Problem was, Chuck chucked a football as though he were wearing brass knuckles.

Before I could say "Fuck the coach," Dave Mcferren, Keith's brother, whom I had not seen since my Red Knight playing days slid onto the bleacher beside me. To me Dave hadn't changed looks after all those years had passed, and I supposed me the same to him. Or maybe we could recognize each other so readily because we shared some metaphysical aural sense. I introduced Dave to Debbie and was going to argue my case to Dave about Bobby's lack of quarterbacking time to Dave, who had already been well informed of the controversy from all the talk at the mill.

"What's Bobby's number?" Dave asked.

"Nineteen," I replied, and before I could say "Fuck the coach" for the 19th time, Humes was suddenly laying upon the ground in pain.

Play was stopped. Out trotted Chuck Rex, another former teammate of mine, to administer aid to the mysteriously injured player. A couple of minutes later, Rex helped Humes hop one-legged off the field as Bobby trotted out as quarterback. He immediately threw six complete passes to lead the Red Knights into scoring position.

I would like to report Bobby rallied his team to a come-from-behind victory over their hated rivals. That miracle would not happen until the end of the following season. What I did know and so did Debbie and I suspected Dave suspected, too, was that Keith touched down on the twenty-yard line that evening and gave the kid named Chuck wearing the numeral 12 a celestial gut punch and this Chuck's last name was not Andrews.

Later that evening inside my house, a beer in one hand, a cigarette in the other, headphones covering my ears, listening to Paul McCartney croon "Yesterday," I realized Keith McFerren had somehow stolen home again and reached me, saying "I got your back, buddy, forever, just like a soul twinkie."

OLLIE OLLIE IN COME FREE

We celebrated summer every summer day. We spent those golden-green days at the swimming pool, at the ballfields, tennis courts, creeks, treehouses, campgrounds, neighborhood backyards, even playing games in side streets, always outdoors. We played Release the Belgium every chance we could. Our fathers had a demand-mantra back then: "Either stay inside or outside!" Obviously, we chose the obvious. Summer lasted until the day after Labor Day, and on that mournful day, we trudged to school on foggy, dewy, grumpy mornings.

It was day and night and night and day and the sum of all our summers rolled into one, and I thought I would be young forever. Young, I am back celebrating a memorial Labor Day.

We celebrated the end of summer in the Center of the Universe in the center of town—Toronto, Memorial Park; Toronto, Ohio, a city back then of 7-plus thousand, a town I like to think the Canadian city is named after.

I believe T-town mothers had something to do with the end-of-summer celebration. We were one-car, one-television, one set of parents those days, and almost all of our moms went by the title Housewife on the Official U.S. Census, Warden on the unofficial census at the family residence.

Maybe most T-townie mammas had some kind of conspiracy going in regards to the renewal of our nine-month confinement to school, even if it meant someday in the future we offspring would have to hike seven miles in hip-high snow, uphill both ways, sometime having to wade chest-high, river rat-infested waters during flood season. We would be out of their house and out of their curlers.

That was before four-lane Ohio Route 7 made an island out of the Center of the Universe, where and when eccentric was the norm, peopled by people known only by their nicknames like Doughnuts,

Henpecker and Flap, when T-town was a one-pizza-shop town and the air so thick you could have seasoned your grandma's potato salad with it, and Mr. Marion Ross, a full-time bus driver, was the head groundskeeper at Memorial Park and did not take any crap from any kids on the bus or upon the grounds, part time or full time.

The sole town shelter house those days rested memorably in Memorial Park within green shadows of the forest canopy, nestled upon a gentle slope overlooking tar-graveled Ridge Avenue. The oaken ark structure was surrounded by islets of initial-tattooed, weathered-gray picnic tables, nearly each complemented with old-fashioned cast-iron sandstone grills. And in the northeast corner of this forgotten parcel leaned the lean-tos the City called the ladies' and gentlemen's restrooms, historically the last public outhouses in T-town City; the only running water coming through their roofs, historically the only place and time *gentleman* and *lady* were used in any part of the four-mile flood plain shaped like a wine skin.

Below, across the tarpits, sat the tennis court and its *No Profanity* signs, and below the courts and a Jolly Green Giant terrace or two lay the Little League field, its outfield arced by a red snow fence and its sandy clay infield flanked by blue-blocked dugouts and a drinking fountain that geysered like Old Unfaithful and an most unfaithful gush of geyser spray away were the tippy-toe steps leading down to the baby pool side of the park, in shadows half-day long, the baby pool a saucer with the world's largest salt shaker in its middle, spraying unsalted water.

The main draw of summer stood like a car-tire-shaped structure rimmed with a white-wall interior, and above it loomed a steeple-high high dive from where you and your chums raised hell holy and chummed the water suicidally and splashed sun-drenched spectators with an assortment of cannonballs, can openers, belly smackers and the made-in-only-T-town buttercup. Beside it on the spectator corner of the white-walled oval sat the low diving board, constructed from recycled catapult and slingshot parts and across on the other end, the shallow side, towered the sliding board, made from fiberglass and guillotine steel.

Under the fading tie-dyed sky, when the peek-a-boo sun tucked itself cozy in its celestial bed for the night, I was there in 1966 upon the tippy-toe hill alongside our south end huddle of river rats—Tim Maple, Chuckie Rex, Tim Hagen, Ronnie Paris, the Twins Conlon, Bobby and Mike, all of us standing cool and rakish and unattended. And you would have thought it was the Fourth of July by the way people packed the pool grounds. If I remember correctly, the day was closer to the Fourth of September and kids and grown-ups and the world's oldest teenagers were straddling and clambering and tottering upon monkey bars, jungle gyms, the top of the sliding board, dugouts, shoulders and backs, craning their necks, tippy-toeing from a tippy-toe hill to witness the events inside the white-walled, so-long-ago, once-upon-a-time swimming pool.

It was a good year to stage the annual Labor Day water show, the opening act the crowning of Little Miss Lions Club with the most impartial way, the selecting of the odd-colored rose although I would have been more partial to the selecting of the odd-colored ear of hard corn because we young T-townies would be chucking handfuls of Sloane's Select and Kuhnie's Cocktail Kernels in a mere few weeks, heralding early tricks for trick-and-treat night.

While officials were coronating Little Miss Lions, the Jocko Twins were crowning and clubbing each other with identical fists, spicing their assaults with some odd-colored words. The Tussling Twins were almost as synchronized as the synchronized swimming that came next down below but not as graceful as the water ballet performed by swan-necked, leggy girls, followed with racing and diving contests by dudes sticking their necks out doing pikes with one-and-a-half twists and gainers and other physics-and-gravity-defying dives—enough to give oneself a watery wedgie, although, the Jockos' acrobatics and wedgie weaves would have scored higher in technical difficulty and originality.

The highlight of these water shows was always the clown act, mostly that staged within the pool. Every Labor Day evening, the T-town water clowns would culminate the show with some dude like Soupy Burns riding an old roadster bicycle right off the high dive,

100

slap-splashing into the emerald-green chlorinated water. Somehow, I suspected these wedgie-defying stunts had something to do with the invention of the Bike Jockey Straps.

And then off the monkey bars, the spectator railings, the crescent-cement dedicated benches atop the tippy-toe hill, off the jungle gyms, off some daddies' slumping shoulders, the overpopulated sagging sliding board, dugout roofs, the hair-trigger trapdoor teeter-totter, the Jockos with permanent wedgies off the roll-around ground—we kids and the world's oldest teenagers slid and hopped and clambered and skedaddled and then jostled and shuffled and sauntered up to the tennis courts, illuminated by its once-in-a-year lighting, where awaited, tuning up, T-town's own garage band, out of the garages from all parts of town, the Conspirators, if I recall correctly, and then the girls, with Cher bangs, pony tails and temporary permanents, would dance that cha-cha back-and-forth, side-to-side shuffle they always did at the Youth Harbor, soon joined by a few brave but foot-heavy boys, like Frank Slowikowski, showing the same footwork that caused him to miss second base, and Teddy Elson, definitely not the strong silent type, and Joe Sokol, banned for yet another year from the bowling alley, and Craig Rock and Mark King, ready to rock and rule the dance floor, Bobby Cowlick, twisting as if his ass was soon going to be in a sling; and Muggsy, lucky mugging a dance floor was still not a crime; and on the dance card you could pencil in Danny Baker and Trim Tyler and tack on Patty Cooper and Judy Gobble; and most untactfully tack on Bobby Zamborsky, always up for some flat out fun: case in point, geography teacher Carl Martin, above in the parking lot, soon to discover engine trouble caused by a turnip shoved up his tailpipe; the root of this problem totally oblivious two spaces away to Harry the Hawk Taylor, who will in minutes get his first lead in the Case of the Missing Garbage Cans, the evidence tied securely onto his own rear bumper.

And the Conspirators conspired with the crowd as the *No Profanity* signs went unheeded, shot to shit, as the teen crowd chorused the unofficial and rumored lyrics of "Louie Louie." Alas, more songs passed as the moon lobbed across court like a fuzzy white Slazenger tennis ball with heavy topspin, the dance ending on one last but very long conga line.

From the parking lot, Chuck Andrews revved his Harley, punched out the season, and below from the other side of the court, across from me, George Miller tugged on his lower lip, signaling, "Although you can outflank the rear end of a police cruiser, you cannot outflank the end of summer."

I acknowledged George, tugging my own lower lip, "Ollie ollie in come free."

THE END

A T-TOWN CITY SIX PACK

THE PHANTOM FARTER

We were ensconced at Camp Crumb, a few miles west of T-town City, where at center camp, Troop 46 Scoutmaster Charles Rex had entrusted me to instruct Camp Orientation, or as I had learned to call from my mentors, Billy Rex and Butch Marker, Camping 666.

I had recently earned my rank of Star Scout and my Basket Weaving merit badge, qualifying me to counsel Tenderfoot and Second Class scouts such as Bobby Chadwick, Jeff Daugherty, Harry Cummings, Teddy Elson, Pete Hagen and Shawn Maple the skills, confidence, knowledge and history needed to become a camper worthy of Troop 46 standards. While I introduced myself, modestly stating my qualifications, achievements and conquests in scouting, sports and especially with the chicks coming from at least three different grade schools and two junior highs and two states; other veteran Troop 46 scouts like Billy Sloane, Chuckie Rex, Timmy Maple, Ronnie Paris and John "Yankee" Yaskanich were out clambering, climbing, crawling and stalking along the crags, cliffs, crevices, fissures, monoliths and booby traps, the camp site itself draped within the hairy knuckled knots of choking grape vines, by some accounts poisonous, descending in clusters like fiendish webs spun by monstrous prehistoric spiders—all in all, providing a most wholesome ambience for the stealthy, strategic, challenging team-oriented game of Release the Belgium, the teams captained by Maple and Rex Jr. perhaps stretching this competition as far as Orsini's Leap and Scaffold Rock.

Meanwhile, camp cooks Dennis Cich and Tim Hagen, ladled out into the untarnished mess kit tins of the eager newbies heaping helpings of locust stew, so named because when properly done is left to simmer 17 years. This camp chefs' version took 17 minutes and some odd seconds.

Oddly enough, these tenderfoots gobbled down the not-so-tender stew as though it were their next to last meal.

From the near distance, beneath the densest shadows, came the utmost feral shrieking and caterwauling, some of which I feared released from some tortured species other than from those participating in an average game of Release the Belgium.

I wanted to earn these newbies' trust, their respect, to put them at ease while at the same time enriching their unfertile psyches with the rich oral traditions of St. Francis Troop 46, consisting of altar boys, choir singers, paper boys, part-time lumberjacks. An eerie blood-orange glow from the pulsating campfire danced across the rapt countenances of my audience as I reached deep within my own psyche to evoke my narrator's voice, a smooth resonating tenor confirming I was accustomed to placing my right hand upon a stack of sacred "Archie Comic Books" while bearing testimony.

It all started as your traditional camping story, one that captured these Boy Scouts' rapt attention with a masterful yarn of the hook-handed madman who had escaped from the local asylum. As I paused for dramatic effect, Some Tenderfoots and even a few Second Classers were leaning forward on their haunches, squirming, biting their fingernails, loosening their collars and patting their brows clueing me they were obviously unraveled or that the locust stew finally hit them.

"And then a shredding sound came from the canvas roof of the convertible. The sultry young blonde looked up and—"

"Who cut the cheese?" cried Teddy Elson, a fifth-year Tenderfoot, his voice whiney from pinching his nose.

A chorus of "ughs" encircled me.

Reacting as any veteran camp counselor would, I called, "Press the digerator."

Immediately twelve solo hands shot up, thumbs planted firmly upon foreheads. Mine made 13.

I looked each scout in the eyes, one by one, my scowl suggesting the retribution of an unappreciated cook. No one claimed authorship for the malodorous aroma wafting throughout camp.

I circled these greenhorns slowly, sniffing for any trace of the miscreant; then I took stage again. "Since no one claims responsibility for this taciturn toot—and it was indeed silent but deadly—I must assume it can be only the work of the Phantom Farter."

Again, I paused for dramatic effect. Then I paced slowly across my moss and lichen stage under the darkening, dappled forest canopy as I unraveled the nose-curdling details.

"You see, the man who would become the Phantom Farter, Funky Firman, was wrongly accused of murdering two young lovers in a car at roadside on a dark, secluded lane just outside T-town, not much more than a prosthetic hook shot away from where we are presently camping. Funky Firman stood trial and was found guilty and sentenced to the gas chamber, although the prosecution could not find the murder weapon, rumored to be a sharp-pointed metallic object—much like a hook.

"Come execution day, Funky Firman had a most unusual request: a bowl of Van Camps baked beans, a side of sauerkraut for his last meal and a bag of dried apricots for dessert. They say most condemned men are too frightened, too nervous, too bewildered to eat any of their last meals, but not Funky Firman. He even licked his eating utensils clean.

"Inside the gas chamber, moments before the executioner was to humanely put Funky Firman down for the eternal ten count, the warden asked the condemned if he had any parting words to utter.

"'Here stands before you,' Funky said, 'an innocent man soon to die from the inhalation of lethal gas.' Funky pointed to the warden, to the preacher, to the witnesses, to the jail keep, to the executioner, to the gas chamber repairman. 'After death, I shall have my revenge on you all and those who have wrongly sent me here, and I shall evoke a most repulsive death unto their sons and daughters and generations to follow.'

"A guard clasped the upper arm of the handcuffed Funky when suddenly erupted the foulest fart of all time, immediately staggering and gagging those inside the chamber. 'Remember that smell,' Funky growled. 'An eye for an eye. A tooth for a tooth. Gas for gas.'

"Those were the last mortal words issued by Funky Firman.

"As the months passed, most everyone in T-town forgot about the execution of Funky Firman. Those who did think occasionally about him knew they had sentenced the right person because no more murders of young lovers at roadside occurred during that period.

"Sometime later, the big wedding arrived: the union between Nick Yanik and Singing Kate at St. Francis Church in T-town. Moments before Kate's father prepared to kiss her away, the father's face screwed into gnarled knots of agony. He staggered one step, two stepped another, gasped, pinched his nose, then swooned face first to the cold ungiving granite aisle. Everyone thought the father of the bride had fainted from nervousness, from the heat inside the church, from the anxiety of paying the reception bill, from the bachelor party at the White Front Cafe the night before, but soon the most repugnant miasma drifted over those in attendance as if Father Cappelli himself had issued it instead of traditional wedding incense. Doc Shaefer, a guest of the would-be bride, rushed to the father's aid, rolled him over and seconds later pronounced the father had fallen victim to a deadly dose of essence of ass.

"The deceased father was none other than Joe Hitchcock, the very judge who passed the gas sentence upon Funky Firman.

"After an intensive investigation, T-town detective, Abie Miller, concluded Judge Hitchcock met his demise from some phantom farter. The name lingered on like the aftertaste of authentic homemade locust stew.

"Months later, on a pumpkin-frosted night, two young lovers swapped spit passionately inside a '64 Chevy Impala, parked at a little, secluded, shady night spot called the Slag Pile. They did not know what invisible force had hit them.

"There were no slashes in the white canvass roof. There were no scratch marks left on the cherry red enamel paint. There was not the telltale hook left dangling from the driver's door.

"T-town detective Miller concluded the heinous act occurred as though the Phantom Farter had stuck his ass on the exhaust pipe of the Chevy. Johnny Wasco and Dotty Nottingham, a jurist son and a jurist daughter of the trial--The State Versus Funky Firman-- succumbed, the coroner declared, to acute fart asphyxiation.

"One by one, the Dark Prince of Flatulence assassinated associates of that fateful trial. No one from it was safe without wearing a clothespin. The protective device worked and evolved, designer clothes pins making a fortune for Richie Wallace Jewelry and Pawn Shop. Days, months and then years flew by like a 17-minute locust stew until the memory of the Ghostly Gasser remained only a passing fancy.

"And then washers and dryers became affordable; the market on designer clothes pins went crashing like Joe Hitchcock on a marble floor.

"Soon came the unthinkable. Another T-town troop—48-- camping with their beloved leader, Scoutmaster Gary Hawkins, at these very grounds was overtaken by the Reeker of Revenge. Twelve boys and Mr. Hawkins consisted of the unluckiest number of them all—thirteen. Rain pelted the troop like bean-shooters beans shot from a 50-story high theater balcony, forcing them inside their big canvass structure, one made of hook-proofed canvass. They called this tent the Whoopee Pad.

"They made the best of their situation, singing Kumbayas and many familiar Boy Scout camping ballads.

"By all accounts the Whoopee Pad was drafty and well ventilated, except on this forsaken night. Jimmy Orsini, First Class Scout, sandlot steady quarterback and captain of the T-town chess club, wailing an inspired tune about Mrs. Sweeny's bloomers, became stuck in mid-note as a stench overwhelmed the troop. They dashed for the tent flap.

"After scout's *honor* and *courage*, the troop forgot the most sacred scout attribute-- *courtesy*. They also shot to hell and back *bravery* and *reverence* as all of them emerged at the tent flap at the same time, cussing like bungee jumpers, elbowing and jostling one another for the exit. Like worms squirming through a single hole in a Damon's yogurt container, the troop toppled onto one another outside into the cool night air, refreshed by the purging rain.

"But it was too late. One by one, those young campers succumbed to a lethal overdose of flatulence, all except Scoutmaster Hawkins, who turned out was the only one present in the Megafart Massacre not of direct lineage of those involved in the Firman trial 20 years before, on the very same date."

I glanced at my official Boy Scout watch, both hands pointing to 12—midnight. "Make that 40 years to the day, boys. Not to worry. Some people say Scoutmaster Hawkins invented the press-the-digerator technique that fateful camping trip, and this action was the true reason the Phantom Farter failed to tally the 13th victim. So, remember this knowledge whenever something smells suspicious emanating from some unaccountable author in your sleeping bag tonight.

"Off to the tents with you. Lights out at 0015. Pleasant dreams."

Moments later, all tortured sounds in the near distance subsiding to familiar soft moans and whimpers, I remembered I needed to retrieve something from my backpack, hanging from a tree branch to keep it safe from raccoons, river rats and other furry marauders. I flashed on a penlight and directed its beam at the contents inside the sack. I shoved past the half ice tong I had forged into a crescent shape, beneath my stash of "Archie Comics" and snaked my hand to the bottom, pulled out a bag of dried apricots and a thermos filled with steamy Van Camps baked beans mixed with sauerkraut. I ate the delicious concoction with the spoon from my official Boy Scout kit, finished the bag of fruit, savored the unusual but delicious pairing and then retired to the tent sheltering my crew. I had a gut feeling a few Boy Scouts were going to be a little edgy for the night.

CROWIN'

"Neither a lender nor a borrower be" was one of my dad's stock sayings, though I suspected he had borrowed most of his stock sayings like "money doesn't grow on trees" and "money is burning a hole in your pocket" and "your eyes are bigger than you stomach." Dad had a shoebox load of stock sayings but no stock in the strongbox.

Needless to say, I didn't take much stock in his stock sayings.

I did learn a different kind of *lend-lease*, the honor system: It would be my honor to test any piece of sporting equipment that wasn't secured with at least ten-feet of one-inch steel chain attached to three tons of reinforced concrete.

There was this rowboat beached upon the shore of the abandoned marina in the south end of T-town City, where the rusty tub we called the "Queen Mary" still floundered like the world's slowest sinking ship, maybe because it was afloat on a waterway that more resembled the world's slowest quick sand than quick currents. The rowboat had a much better fate: being burrowed in a mucky substance some might have called a shoreline.

I called the rowboat *Old Barnsides*.

It obviously was an older, ventilated model probably designed to reduce drag, although I suspected not the kind of drag used for sounding-the-bottom operations.

Old Barnsides had two oars at the ready. Looking at *Old Barnsides* under a new sun trying to poke through the morning pollution, I had a somewhat sinking feeling what my father had in mind when he uttered his stock saying, "too poor to even float a loan."

Back then, the Steubenville, Ohio Metropolitan Area held the esteemed title of Most Polluted City in the USA, and six miles north, the suburb T-town, though under-documented and highly suspected

111

from the dearth of Social Security contributions, held the stinky distinction of being the World Capital of the World's Oldest Teenagers, and no teenager was any teenier than Singing Dick.

With an old piece of driftwood, I pried *Old Barnsides* out of the muck onto the greasy, jaded, gray waters of the Ohio River. I loaded into this drafty craft my fishing gear and tackle that I had collected over the last few years, some of which I actually paid with paper boy money, others from the unwritten though inviolable time-true laws such as squatter's rights, bad memory, dubs-up and finders-keepers.

Eerily, craftily, I oared the airy craft downstream against counterpoint waves lapping the prow like a puppy begging to hump your leg. Humping, I stroked into the gritty, sulphur-sooted wind toward a force much windier though somewhat what I called getaway clean—Singing Dick.

Singing Dick was about thirty-teen at the time. His real name was Richard, but if you called him that he would pay you no more attention than if you had offered him a job. I am 60-teen-percent certain T-townies called him Singing Dick because he was always crowin' a medley of Motown songs. Forty-teen-percent of me thought maybe Dick got the Singing moniker because the town of 7,500 was full of dicks, many of which loitered in front of Islay's and at the street corners of downtown, wanting to borrow your milk money, expressing the promise of interest, a very keen interest to cut out your gizzard with a switchblade.

I picked up the Mouth of Motown at the mouth of Sloane's Creek where he stepped into *Old Barnsides*. When I offered him an oar, he said, "No thanks, I am trying to quit," while sliding onto a plank that more resembled a teeter-totter than a bench. He was wearing a white t-shirt with a rolled-up sleeve bulging from a cigarette case, tight blue jeans and scuffed, pointy black boots. His brown hair was slicked back into a ducktail, fashionable back in the day when he first turned teenager. He had one of the softest, most sedate voices I had ever heard from a grownup teenager, one that could soften even a tone or two from crowin' or crying. Besides his

112

voice, what stood out like a sore hitch-hiking thumb about T-town's top teenager was his chiseled countenance, I suppose from years of practice.

I pushed off shore with one paddle and veered out into the grimy currents with the other while currently Dickie was hitching a free ride.

"You got a smoke I can bum?" Dickie asked.

"No, I quit smoking months ago," I replied.

Dickie was the answer to the Surgeon General's admonition to quit smoking. Over the years, Dickie had bummed so many smokes some guys would rather quit than give him one more.

"You know I'm good for it," he said, in his about-to-cry voice.

He had a look on his face suggesting someone replaced his baloney with pickle loaf. "Can I borrow a fishing pole?" he asked.

I handed him a cheap spin-cast outfit I had obtained on the old finders-keepers clause.

"How about a couple of lures? You know I'm good for them."

I rowed us downstream to the tip of Brown's Island where I cast a medley of lures along weed beds while Dickie crowed a medley of Motown tunes. I don't think the fish were all that fond of Dickie's crowin' and probably scattered all the way to Detroit.

I gave Dickie a look subtly telling him to shut his crow hole. I wanted to duct tape his tear ducts.

"What's the matter, Bobby?" Dickie asked in a voice as soothing as Vicks VapoRub and as effective as rubbing it on the soles of your feet. "How about crowin' a little with me?"

"Can't," I said, in a not-so-soul-smooth-VapoRub-sole voice, "It will spook the fish."

"Not my crowin.' Just last week I caught a lake trout this big." He spread out his hands nearly arm's length, what I was certain a new state record had there been any of this species in the state, his splayed arm knocking the twice-borrowed pole right into the water. It disappeared in a T-town second, as if the textured surface of the Ohio snapped itself shut.

Dickie slipped his cigarette case from his shirt sleeve and offered me a smoke. I held out my hand and then quickly pulled back.

"How about lending me another pole?" Dickie asked, in a voice so soft you could sink in it. "You know I'm good for it." Even though his voice was soft as Charmin, I was pretty sure he was full of shit.

I had two rods remaining, one of which I actually bought with paper route money from the local hardware store, Kuhnie's. I had this not so soft feeling in my gut that fishing was going to be the second thing I gave up in recent months.

"Okay," I said, handing him the extra rod and reel, "Be careful, this one's been awful lucky."

Dickie stood up, wobbling in the back of *Old Barnsides*. With any luck, he would topple into the river and at least provide some kind of entertainment I could actually enjoy.

"I'll do right by it," Dickie said, his Kleenex voice promising to clean me out. He held a hand up holding what was usually an invisible microphone, this time trembling from the strain of hoisting some invisible dead weight. "Two weeks ago, I caught me a largemouth bass-- 22 inches by the tape. Then I caught me a carp-- 30 inches by the tape." His hand and arm still struggling with invisible trophy fish, or the world's heaviest microphone, Dickie's voice started straining as though under pressure from squeezing the Charmin. "A week before that, I got me a carp-- 40 inches." He hesitated several seconds, I suppose, for dramatic effect. "By the tape. And the week before, a channel cat two inches."

"What?!" I shrieked. "Two inches—by the tape?!"

"No, from the ground."

Dickie looked at me nodding and primping as if he were the second coming of James Dean starring in the flick *Rebel Without A Job.*

"I'll do you right, Bobby," Dickie said, his voice so soft I half-expected Johnson's Baby Powder to puff out of it. "I'll make good, you'll see." Then I thought powder did puff out his crowin' canal. It wouldn't have surprised me a bit if too much Johnson's Baby Powder was another thing that stunted your growth.

I paddled. Dickie sang. I paddled us to an off channel between Brown's Island and the West Bank while Dickie crowed off-key. Here the water averaged about a four-foot depth; if Dickie so happened to drop the rod into the water we had a blind chance to snag it back into the boat.

"Can I have another lure?" Singing Dick asked, already rummaging inside my tackle box. He withdrew my favorite lure, held it up like a two-inch trophy minnow. "I won't lose it to a snag," he said in his about-to-cry voice. "I promise if I do, I'll buy you a whole new tackle box full of them."

Dickie was right—he did not lose the lure to a snag, at least in the traditional sense. He looped his first cast around a tree limb, behind us upon the shore.

We watched that lure slowly pendulating from that limb, glistening like a gold tooth of some dude swinging from the gallows.

I gave Dickie a look I borrowed from Mother Mary Paula as she was about to test a brand-new steel-edged ruler upon a mess of knuckles.

"Don't worry, Bobby. I got out of worse ones before. I'll bet you five dollars I won't lose that lure."

Dickie yanked on the fishing line to the near breaking point. Then he jerked and came the nearest to sweating and overstraining in his thirty-teen years. That lure broke free, all right, the 25-pound-test monofilament snapped and directly toward Singing Dick flew the tree limb.

For a dude whose fastest pace was usually in a line for a free lunch, Dickie reflexively parried the battering-ram-sized projectile with the twice-borrowed rod, splintering the rod into a thousand and three uncollectible pieces. The lure fell harmlessly into the boat, right by the scruff of his boots.

He held up the lucky lure and swept his other hand toward me, palm splayed wide open. Although I was pushed to the snapping point of 100-pound-test, I reached into my back pocket, pulled out my wallet and slapped five bucks into Dickie's totally uncalloused palm.

Already crowin', he stuffed the Lincoln into his tight jeans pocket, unrolled his shirt sleeve and produced another cigarette.

"I think I'll have one of those now," I said.

"I would give you one, but it's my last."

I put the oars in the water and stroked so hard I nearly teetered Dickie off this teeter-totter bench and I kept trying to do so all the way to the Mouth of Sloane's Creek, where the Mouth of Motown hopped out, five dollars richer.

"Hey, Dickie, I'll pick you up at the same time next week," I said. "You know I'm good for it."

"And I'll be waiting with two brand new rods and reels for you."

Singing Dick heeled around and pimped up an embankment leading to South River Avenue. I was pretty certain he would stand there, thumbing, until someone picked him up. Halfway up the slope, Dickie paused to light up his newest last cigarette.

Plenty of daylight still remained plus I had one rod and reel and my favorite fishing lure. Or did I?

I searched everywhere inside *Old Barnsides* for that lure, pretty certain where it had disappeared. I looked for Dickie again, already beyond the trees, out of sight. I could still hear him. He sure was crowin'.

I had the remainder of the day, the entire Ohio River and a boat all to myself. I was crowin' and casting and casting and crowin' Singing Dick's top ten greatest greasy hits. All I wanted was one measly huge one one-hit wonder of a fish, a tape-measure legend. And I sang and sang and snag-- Sometimes I think the plots of our lives come down to a mere celestial typo.

Lure free, free of T-town's oldest teenager, free like a hippy mariner, I lay back in *Old Barnsides*, my head and legs propped upon the antique oak planks, and I borrowed some sapphire from the sky, and borrowed some emerald from the harp-shaped hills, and borrowed some gold from the sun, borrowed some spice from the peppery wind, bummed some diamonds from the glittering waves, and I said to myself, "finders keepers."

GEMMING THE GYM CITY

A certain bit of lost information regarding George "Gabby" Kunzler, a much-celebrated athlete and coach, haunted me like a hook-handed urban legend. I could not quite get a finger on it.

I had Mr. Kunzler for Driver's Education and he pretty much didn't do much gabbing except when one of us was coasting through a stop sign, speeding up for a yellow light or straying toward a fire hydrant. About the only times I remember his saying anything at all was when some driver's ed student left a few molten Milk Duds laying upon his seat. Gabby hopped off of the co-pilot's seat, a dozen Milk Duds pressed into the pressed seat of his blue suit pants, cussing a blue streak stretching from one end of town to the other. Then there was the time he looked into the rearview mirror and caught Ronnie Paris and Ruthie C. making out as though they finally had learned something from French class.

I did know from talking with Jay Smith Sr. and other T-town City old-timers that Gabby's athletic feats occurred sometime during the 1920s and 30s when this sleepy and much isolated town recorded its lore mostly by word of mouth, often under the influence, and not academic. I knew of only one person who could clarify the matter causing me this consternation, and he was Teeter Rawson, a venerable octogenarian who knew a little something about everything that had happened in the Gem City since the day he could stand upright in bib overalls.

Teeter's discourse often roamed into tangents and tended to spin the same yarns over and over, like the time he tackled hometown hero and Football Hall of Famer Clarke Hinkle all by himself, and he repeated them as though he were narrating the stories for the first time. You dared not interrupt him, at least not until he was finished, usually happening when he fell asleep, and then you had better tiptoe away before you wouldn't know, as Teeter always said, "grits from granola."

My hands at ten-till-two upon the steering wheel, a few empty Milk Dud boxes scattered upon the passenger seat, I drove to Teeter's rustic cabin at Wildcat Hollow, just outside the north end of town. A rickety old wooden bridge most dudes wouldn't attempt on a dare and a bet and with six-pack muscles spanned Holler Creek leading to his shack. Driving across the bridge, I suddenly suspected Gabby had been so taciturn because he suffered from the anatomical anomaly by which the butt bone is connected to the lip bone. And my butt was tighter than trick Tupperware crossing those wobbly, weathered, gray planks that would have served better as a makeshift roof.

I found Teeter rocking upon his wooden rocker under an overhang that was sagging from lack of support—structural and financial. Teeter was wearing his familiar frayed, shin-high, baggy bib overalls and time-faded, blue denim railroad cap, the bill casting a shadow over his perennial wizened five o'clock shadow. Although I had not seen Teeter for what seemed like a Locust Man's lifetime, I could still see Teeter maintained the same family values: that he lived a simple lifestyle, that he and nature were one and that he thought soap and teeth were overrated. Teeter attributed his good fortune and health to wearing his lucky underwear. Of course, I don't have to tell you how often he wore them.

Having hunted squirrels and trapped river rats a few times with Teeter in the forest surrounding Wildcat Hollow, I needed no self-introduction. "I have a question or two to ask you about Gabby Kunzler," I said.

Teeter gnawed upon his lower lip like a river rat testing doughball and before I could finish my question he said in his stringy voice, "Kunzler, Gabby, yep. I member him. He's the guy they named the gymnasium after—the very first one in these here parts." He rubbed his stubbled chin, then said, "Maybe it was the lights they put up inside the gym. Anyhow, nobody in this here town could spell much; so, they shortened it to 'gym.' That's how come the town beens named Gem City. Why if I misspelled a word and used bad grammar, my pappy would of warshed my mouth out with

119

fryin' oil and paddled my rear end so flat you could of skipped rocks off'n it."

Teeter stood up and turned around to display his back britches, and I could see that it was definitely more plank-like than that rotten, warped, dangling overhang under which I now stood and maybe a bit sounder than his bridge. His glib tongue suggested Teeter might have slipped off the grammar train few times during his day.

Teeter leaned back in his rocker again and mumbled, "Gym City, Gem City. Come to think of it, they wasn't much good at pronunciating, either.

"I member the year the gem of this here gym was built, the spring of '36—the very same of the Great Warsh. It was the winter afore when I'd walk seven miles to school with snow up to the bottoms of my bibs-- and that was just to reach the bus stop. That snow never hampered them construction workers a' tall Course, we had real workers back then, not like the bunch of sissy boys today, take off three days for a hang nail, then expect to get paid.

"They completed the gym just afore the big thaw, and it rained six straight days and nights and all that snow melted. The river flooded all the way uppen Wildcat Holler.

"I was fishin' right at this here spot, catchin' more carp and mudcats than you could shake a willer stick at. My ma and pappy and the rest of my kin was trapped up the holler some ways, but I was payin' them no never mind cause the fishin' was so good. Ain't every day you can fish off'n your own front porch.

"I member the very moment I was recollectin' bout the time I tackled Clarke Hinkle all by myself—I'll have to tell you bought that sometime. The bridge warshed away and out where it should of been gushed the biggest fish I ever did see. I shook my noggin' a few times and rubbed my peepers. That weren't no ordinary fish but none other than the Oswango Monster.

"I member my grandpappy tole me bout him afore and how'd he harpooned the monster square in the eye. And his granddaddy afore him seed the monster when he was tradin' with the great Chief Logan."

Teeter leaned back in his rocker again, his head tilted toward the dangling overhang. I thought perhaps some dust and debris had cascaded onto his grizzled mug. "Logan's real name in Mingo talk was Ta-Ja-Uh-Tee-Ta-Ja, but the all the white folks called him Logan acause it was easier to name their streets after."

Teeter leaned back again. This time some dust and debris did fall onto his mug, but he paid it no more attention than he would a bar of Irish Spring.

"Oswango—that's what Chief Logan and his tribe called the Ohio River them days.

"This monster hit like Clarke Hinkle going off tackle against the New Cumberland Bulldogs. I seed this is the very same Oswango Monster cause he got just one eye and it had this real ornery look like the bear that done bit Ole Yeller. Some old timers called him Long Jaws acause he had more teeth than the Fuller Brush man and yellower. This fish was as long and thick as the chiminey at Kaul Clay and was covered with seaweed from head to tail.

"I onced tackled Clarke Hinkle all by myself so I weren't afraid a' tall of any oversized fish. I said to him, 'I spose you got some unfinished business for what my grandpappy done did to you.'

"The Oswongo didn't take none too kindly to that remark and no sooner than you can think 'I'm awearin' my lucky underbritches' he swatted his slimy, scaly tail upon the surface, soakin' me clear up to my bib straps and knockin' me flat on my flat can. I twisted round and went to skedaddle inside the cabin, but that splash-- it slammed the door shut tighter than a jar of homemade gherkins.

"'Well, now you're done for,' I said to myself.

"I was stuck like a piece of cheap steak between your teeth, what I recollect of them, with nothin' more'n a hickory switch I carved into a fishin' pole to defend myself. Knowin' he ain't got

121

much of a periphree vision, I skip back and forth across this here porch, trapped like a river rat. Suddenly the beast came lurchin' at me and chomped right through the post that onced held up the roof at this here end of the porch. Made of locust, too. Well, next comes down the stone chiminey just like Clarke Hinkle when I tackled him all by myself, conkin' the monster right on his slimy, green head; stunnin' him for a few seconds and as quick as a tiddy wink I jousted the blunt end of my fishin' pole right into his good eye. The beast was thrashin' and mewin' something awful like somebody done put its balls into a headlock. Then in a tiddy wink, maybe two later, the monster got real quiet-like and slinked off into the muddy water. That's the last anybody done seed or heard tell of the Oswango Monster."

Teeter coughed, and was clearing his throat, sounding as if a hairball the size of the monster's eye was lodged in his gullet, when I remembered a question about Gabby Kunzler, that he might have once pitched an exhibition game against the Homestead Grays of the old Negro League. "About Gabby Knuzler?" I asked.

"Yep, I member him. He was that guy they named the gymnasium after, called it a gem acause it had lights inside…"

Teeter repeated the story three or four times with some colorful variations. Then finally he toppled over like the chimney that took out the Oswango Monster, my cue to tighten up my own two ass hemispheres and flee across the bridge before Teeter awakened or the bridge surrendered to gravity.

My right hand on the wheel at two o'clock, my left quashing my nerves with fresh Milk Duds, the candy tasting a little like a mix of grits and granola, I drove at a speed that would have evoked a blue response or two from the tight-lipped tutor of T-town City High so that I could write Teeter's story word for word before I forgot it.

I did go fishing at the mouth of Croxton's Run a few days later. I was working a deep-diving crankbait when I heard this splash upstream sounding like the time Ruthie C. crashed the driver's ed car into a fire hydrant. In a Teeter wink I felt something tightening down the back of my Dockers. I leaped like Gabby Kunzler squatting upon a couple dozen melted Milk Duds and then I hitched a ride upon the Blue Streak Special. Luckily for me, I was wearing my lucky underwear, and I need not tell you how often I wear them.

MUSCLE BEACH

In T-town City there was one bad dude whom T-townies called Kishka, named after a polka about blood pudding, written and recorded by Frankie Yankovich in the 1960s. Kishka added the feminine French article *La* to enhance status and dignity to his reputation. La Kishka was neither Slavic nor French and most likely totally unaware that the article was feminine, and he was not especially fond of polkas because he considered any form of dance sissy stuff. About the only things he liked to do were fish and fight, and not necessarily in that order.

I first met La Kishka in the summer of '68, the result of a foolish whim to venture into the north end of town, believing the bass were meaner on the other side and that La Kishka was as much urban legend north of Main Street as was the neckless Hanging Head in my neck of the woods. There he was, bigger than 3D, sitting upon a log a little downstream from where Croxton's Run dumped into the greasy rainbow surface of the Ohio River. The rod tip of his extra stout fishing rod rested upon a forked tree branch planted firmly into the silty, sandy shore. La Kishka had short, wavy brown hair that framed his face, his jaw looking to me like the thin end of a speed bag, though I was certain it was anything but.

La Kishka was wearing a white ribbed tank top, cut-off blue jeans and was sockless in his black Converse sneakers. Grimacing, both hands pushing together in front of his barreled chest, La Kishka appeared to be performing some type of isometric exercise.

"How are you doing?" I accosted him.

"What are you looking at?" he growled in a deep grotto voice.

Before I could reply, he growled so deep you could have dug a hole halfway to China, "You want to do something about it?" He jumped up, brandishing clenched fists. I could see they were both equally, heavily scarred.

Just then his rod took a dive, I am sure like several of his would-be victims. La Kishka swooped upon the rod butt and yanked so hard the rod whistled air, leaves fluttering above us. Seconds later, his rod went limp as if he himself had put his fishing rod into his infamous sleeper hold.

He kicked the ground a few times, then the log upon which he had been sitting and then stomped and snorted and cussed cuss words unknown at my end of town, every other cuss word punctuated with *punk!* Finally, he calmed down.

Calmly he said, "I don't like your looks."

A few nuns, teachers and especially my three sisters did not like my looks, but that was no reason to rearrange them. Still I did not take any lip from them and I was not about to take any lip off someone named after a polka with a feminine French article preceding it; so I decided to take the cerebral approach. "I will hit you so hard I will splice your genes," I said as if reading from a science text book.

The Angry Angler had this look on his mug suggesting he had slept through one too many of Mr. Kalivoda's science classes as he reached around patting his backside to determine whether his pants were split.

"Make me," he said.

Now, I was really getting Darwinian, "I don't make monkeys, I sell them."

Well, the Fighting Fisherman's face turned a red as a baboon's ass. "I'll tell you what," he growled, "You go ahead and throw the first punch." He clasped both hands behind his back and stuck out his jaw.

I continued the Darwinian approach: I naturally selected my dominant right fist and punched La Kishka dominantly on the chin, knocking him into carp territory.

He floundered in the water for a few moments; then emerged rubbing his chin. "It's a good thing I promised a couple of broads I would catch supper or else I would pound you so hard on top of the head you would have to look up to see down."

He nearly laughed at this flash of wit as though he had invented it—could even remember it-- then said, "I am going to take you." He paused to look upstream, squinting in the eastern sunlight, "to the discharge at the power plant. Caught a fifty-pounder last week."

The quarter-mile trek along shore turned out a bit slower than I had anticipated because the Ringside Rod and Reeler held out his arms as though he were lugging a suitcase containing all the fish he had ever caught with one arm, the other a keg containing all the blood he had inflicted, not to mention his Converses slurping and slipping from all that gummy Ohio River water.

A boater upstream saw us and promptly oared around, stroking his skiff as if he were in gold medal contention at the Summer Olympics.

La Kishka pivoted and thumbed toward the oarsman. "See that guy, Mike Melnik. I beat him up in second grade, made him cry."

Veins were popping out everywhere upon the Angry Angler when we at last reached the discharge spilling from the power plant where two boys about ten and eleven years of age were sitting in fold-up canvas chairs, fishing. LaKishka promptly bear-hugged the eleven-year-old and dumped him headfirst into the greasy river. The younger one dove in voluntarily. They took off swimming as if they were in the second heat of the Olympics.

The chairs were a bit too small for La Kishka's ass-kicking butt, but he sat on one anyway and helped himself to the kids' nightcrawlers, squirming like his potential victims inside a galvanized bait bucket.

The Live Bait Liquidator had this remarkable ability to recall in vivid detail the outcome of every fight he had ever undertaken, whether that tussle resulted from fighting or fishing. He even went as far to carve notches into the handles of his Snoopy lunch bucket in grade school and later on the butt of his fishing pole, commemorating his conquests. The cork handle looked as serrated as his knuckles. He claimed as early as second grade he was beating up eighth graders, one while the Scourge of Sandy Shores was wearing his First Holy Communion outfit.

The Great Whitewater Hope held out the cork handle of his Zebco 33 for my admiration, scrolling tenderly with a finger along its length. "This one here was a twenty-pounder. Took him in under two minutes on my special doughball." He scrolled up an inch or so. "Twenty-five-pound carp, two minutes, 13.4 seconds, Jolly Green Giant corn." He pointed a little above the slash denoting the corn-conquered carp. "Then there was the bass—"

"Largemouth?" I asked

"It was after I got done with him. Ernie G. Bass, gave him two fat, bloody lips, fourth grade."

The Public Enemy Number One of Elementary School started on his lunch box trophies. "Benny Driscoll, fifth grade, a black eye and bloody nose. Second grade, Ritchie Allen, two black eyes and a fat lip. Sixth grade, Joe Zamborsky, a cauliflower ear, bloody nose and two front teeth."

Watching his head tilt back, his eye-gouging forefinger stroking the butt of his fishing rod, I thought I saw his perpetual scowl slowly dissolving into a slight, tight-lipped smile. "Basses," he said, his voice a pitch or two higher than usual, "Gave me the best fight of them all."

"That has to be smallmouth," I introjected.

"Hooked them good. Two lefts and two rights, right on the jaw of Ernie G. and his big brother Terry T. Choked them both out at the same time."

Left and right, the Bass Assassin was taking out kids and carp. The crap was getting so heavy I felt my Keds sinking deeper and deeper into the soft shore. Then he jabbered about his hand speed, then that of his feet, boasted he could even outrun nuns.

"I'm into catch-and-release these days," La Kishka said. "They take off running, I catch them and then release the punks from their misery."

I had this sinking gut feeling that the Catch-and-Release Clobberer was just warming up; his kind of routine giving a whole new meaning to *punchline.*

The Fist -and Fish- Fanatic confessed the guys that he beat up came about because they had looked at him the wrong way or simply he did not like their looks. Not surprisingly, he said that when he grew up he wanted to become a police officer or a plastic surgeon.

Somehow during all his gab, we managed to catch a few small carp, which La Kiska returned to the river with some swift, powerful kicks from his Converses.

During a rare moment of silence, La Kishka's line shot out like his famous left jab and as quick as a good, old one-two he jerked the rod so far I thought La Kishka was reaching back for a one-hit-knockout haymaker, his rod doubling over like Lee Ignatz after La Kishka uppercut him in the stomach in third grade.

"Any size?" I asked.

"Can't tell. One hundred pounds, fifty pounds, ten—they all feel the same to me." As if he were watching a film showing his ten greatest knockouts, La Kishka leaned back in his chair, cranking his reel as though he were no more than stirring butter in his popcorn—and he was one Mississippi-one-two-three counting the entire battle. About in 60.3 seconds the Fighting Fisherman lugged onto shore this long, wriggly, slimy, green thing—an eel, maybe 46.4 inches long.

"A snake!" screamed La Kishka, his basement-bottom voice now a few octaves in the penthouse of panic. He leaped up, the chair encased around his ass-kicking ass, and then he stepped into the bait bucket. He took off as if a nun were chasing after him with a

128

customized straight-edge ruler and was going to give him a few extra whacks for good measure.

I released the eel and followed the unusually long strides of the bucket prints leading up a hill.

I found La Kishka at the top, the sun-glistening bucket now pulled over his crown, squirmy nightcrawlers dangling like dreadlocks, the mother of the boys crowning him with the folding chair.

I did not stick around to learn what happened next. I was pretty sure she didn't like my looks, anyway.

THE ABDOMINAL SNOWMAN OF MOUNT KNEE BOW

I had been cruising around the little-known town of Toronto, Ohio, an isolated city of seven-thousand-plus tucked between the Appalachian Foothills as if inside a giant fish bowl, cut off from neighboring West Virginia by the radioactive moat most map makers called the Ohio River.

I was currently researching an as yet untitled book detailing local T-town legends, such as its version of the marathon, what T-townies dubbed the 26er, in which participants had to complete imbibing a libation of twelve ounces or its equivalent from every watering hole stretching from the Welsmar district in the south end to the Dyer Country Club just outside the north end, four miles distance as the crow flies, 26.2 miles as the crow staggers.

Local legend maintained only one person had successfully completed the T-town 26er, one Charlie Eshbaugh, said to do most of his training at a south end elbow bender called the White Front Café. I considered the T-town 26er as much urban myth as that of the hook-handed escapee from the local asylum Cambridge, the Hanging Head of Camp Crumb and the Oswango Monster of Wildcat Holler. In fact, I had my doubts Charlie Eshbaugh even existed.

I set about to do some research on this matter, get a taste for things, so to speak. I did so by stopping at the midtown establishments Gem City Restaurant, George's and Frog's Place, the latter where I could have shouted "zip-a-dee-doo-dah!" to my serendipity encountering city oral historian, the most honorable Teeter Rawson. Fortunately, I had a pen and notebook at the ready and the availability of two bar rags if the need came to be.

Some T-towners might have maintained Teeter drank a little too much, but I maintained he was one of the most reliable sources to reside upon this four-mile flood plain of which some wags called *Tea Town.* To me, Teeter was an optimist who always saw the light at the end of a bottle. He was also sincere, if not entirely accurate, always wearing his heart upon his sleeve and sometimes his chili. Teeter was the one who taught me how T-town got its nickname, Gem City, a play on words from the 20-plus watering holes in town locals called *liver gymnasiums,* those including twenty-some with licenses and some others without the state's stamp of approval, as well as counting the back room of the public library. *Gym City* they called the town.

On this day, Teeter was seeing a lot of light while lightening my wallet, He was parched perched upon his bar stool. I did my best to keep the silver-throated treasure lubricated enough to continue his narrative to the end while I jotted it word for word, except, of course, his recounting the time he tackled Football Hall of Famer Clarke Hinkle all by himself. Fortunately, I found enough dry spots on the bar rags to capture his historic prose.

Somewhere around Teeter's sixth shot of enlightenment, his memory stirred to life, like a swizzle stick in the River Rat, the town's official mixed drink, its ingredients a treasured and much guarded secret. He snapped his bony finger, "Charlie Eshbaugh, I member that feller. He was the pitcher for the White Front Whales softball team. I was there that very afternoon. Theys was warshing down their sorrows after gettin' their cans canned in a tourneement by some team callin' theirselves SAC. 'Sacked by the SAC,' the Jocko Twins kept sayin' over and over, pokin' fun at the likes of Artie Robertson, Hunk Romey, Bob Grant and that knucklehead that threw the losing knuckleball when inside the front door of the White Front Café waddles the Abdominal Snowman from Mount Knee Bow. Why I ain't seen him in pert near a river rat's cat nap.

"He'd come down from Mount Knee Bow, the mountain some folks called that hill rising like one of those Hostess Snocones just south of town. Named it after Chief Knee Bow, they did, of the Bozican Tribe, the Snowman being the last of the Bozicans. About the only thing passed down to the Snowman from his great great

131

grandpappy—Chief Knee Bow, was his legs, bent like a horseshoe, gave him the uncommonest luck and the uncanniest balance. The Snowman was as pale as a Hostess mound, that's how he done got his name, white as the coconut kind and just as flaky. That belly of his was all muscle, thirty pounds worth he done got by doin' nothin' cept sit-ups, crunches and yogi all the time atop the home of his ancestors and got the endurance from searchin' for some mushroom only growin' in Locust Man poop.

"I ain't believed none of that crap bout some special mushroom that gives a gal back her virginity and I sures a hell don't believe in any local winged Big Foot called the Locust Man, no siree.

"But I believed in the Abdominal Snowman, and I was a starin' at him with my own two peepers and he comes in with that Bert Engle feller, who was doin' all the talkin' cause the Snowman didn't want to strain his voice none as he was savin' it to join the oprey someday.

"So, this Bert Engle feller says, 'I'll bet anybody here 100 bucks the Snowman can do 200 sit-ups in less than a minute.' I can see Hunk Romey sittin' on a bar stool, his ears perkin' up at the sound of Engle thumbin' through a wad of money. He swings round and says, 'I'll take that bet,' and slaps five twenties in Bert's hand.

"Art, Buck Brown, Chutch Rock and a few other fellers says they want a piece of that action and afore you could holler half the liver gymnasiums in the Gym City the Snowman cranks out 200 sit-ups with a few gyms to spare.

"Them White Front Whales are shakin' their heads like they just found out the bar maid Karen Henry been waterin' down their River Rats, and Bert says, 'I'll bet anybody here the Snowman can knock anybody on his can before they can the Snowman.'

"The Snowman is just standin' there, wearrin' only his red wraslin' tights with white letterin' across that 12-pack of his sayin' *T-town Cutters;* so, you know he knows somebody, and nobody more perky than that Bert feller wavin' money under their noses like its smellin' salts.

"Art Robertson takes a good whiff of that money and a whiff of a cheeseburger. Art, most White Fronters called *Big Daddy* cause, well let's just say he was a heavy favorite, got that name from doin' all them 12-ounce preacher curls at the White Front Gymnasium. Big Daddy goes at the Snowman like he's the last beer keg in town and the Abdominal just bends over like he's a goin' to tie his size 17s and then springs out and babooms Big Daddy with thirty pounds of belly muscle and Art finds hisself all sprawled out on the floor with the look on his face like somebody done stole the pickle off his cheeseburger.

"Next steps up Bob Grant, shakin' a fistful of dollars like it's the fifth payday of the month when the credit union ain't takin' anythin' out. Everybody called him *The G*, and it ain't from sayin' *Gee Whiz*. Before you could have said *jeepers H. cripes* The G is flat on his can, sayin' 'F this and F that.'

"Then up steps Mark McCart. Some called him *Clyde*. He got the Clyde part down, all right, fresh out of the hoosegow from saltin' a battery, but he ain't got no Bonnie. Clyde dumps a whole shaker of salt over a shoulder while the Snowman sucks in his belly so far you'd be thinkin' he's playin' hunch back for the Notre Dame Fightin' Irish. Clyde goes at the Snowman like he's goin' to knock the white out of him and then salt his wounds, but the Snowman's belly is wound up tighter than the Mummy's under britches and lets it all fly and lets Clyde knows who's who in the hoosegow.

"Then Suitcase Simpson thinks he can handle the Snowman and before you can pick your nose and wipe it off'n the counter, Suitcase is pickin' hisself off the floor and sent packin'.

"Them Whales are forkin' money out left and right and kissin' the floor while the Snowman is dishin' out punishment right and left, the Whales standin' round stiffer than Popeye's spinach dick when suddenly the White Front's front door swings open and in comes steppin' Soupy Burns. Soupy ain't got no ordinary step cause his pointy boots are always pointin' ten till two, cept theys counterclockwise. Them pigeons he's got for feet got that way some fellers say cause he has some kind of set on him, and bearin' all that weight all them years turned his toes inward-like.

"Bert steps up to Soupy and sizes him up from the tips of his cross-eyed toes all the way up-n his pigeon peeps to the top of his greasy kid stuff like he's Clarkie the undertaker undertakin' measurin' Soupy for a casket. Bert steps back with this look on his mug sayin' he ain't goin' to be balancin' his checkbook anytime soon if he tests the likes of Soupy's balance with them pointy toes. With pigeons like that you could see for yourself Soupy could tight-walk across a telephone wire while blowin' smoke rings.

"Besides his toes always pointin' the wrong time of day, Soupy has the reputation as the town's best trick diver, his specialty ridin' a roadster bicycle off'n the high dive of the public swimmin' pool.

"Bert wraps an arm round the round shoulders of the Snowman and says, 'I'll give you five to one odds the Snowman here can out-dive old Soupy.'

"Well, everyone there is takin' that bet cept they are now placin' their money on the Snowman even if it means bettin' five bucks to win six.

"They all leave the White Front, even Karen, wavin' a bar rag like it's some terrible towel, and head up Franklin Street toward the swimmin' pool, ten city blocks away, and along the way gym goers from Skunks, the Flamingo Club and the public library join the procession and put most of their money on the Bouncin' Belly of the Bozicans.

"By the time you can name the other half of the 26er, Soupy's up there atop of that high dive atop of that roadster bicycle, wearin' nothin' other than his lucky underbritches and you can see he's got hisself some special set on him—got that way from takin' the impact of landin' smack dab on the water sittin' on the seat of that red roadster bicycle. His lucky underbritches was the tightest boxers you ever done seed and lookin' like one of those Any Warhol prints with 30 different flavors, includin' my favorite—tomater.

"A big crowd now is gatherin' round the pool watchin' the Snowman warmin' up doin' the impossible-- touchin' his toes. He never even broke out a cold sweat belly-boppin' them White Front Whales. Soupy's up there waitin' for the signal from the judge, fixin' his waist band just right, gets the go-ahead wave and wheels off that high dive smoother than any of them Whales hit the floor and with less splash.

"Sam Wells, the softball umpire, who called the final out on Danny Robertson in the Whales' loss to SAC, is the sole judge, and scores Soupy's dive only a 9.4, sayin' in that Brooklyn accent by way of T-town City of his, 'I just calls them as I sees them and I sees Soupy was grabbin' that set of his on the way down to the water.'

"You can see Soupy's disagreein' with that call, his peepers gettin' all cross-eyed just like his toes, but he ain't sayin' much, justs lights up a Lucky Strike and turns his attention to the Snowman, who is up on the high awaitin' the go-ahead from Sammy Wells. The Snowman chooses usin' the same roadster bicycle and I could see that seat slowly disapearin' between the Snowman's butt cheeks, like it done melted. He pedals anyway, right off'n that high high dive cept he ain't got the set Soupy's got and goes right down to the bottom, eleven feet in the drink and ain't comin' up.

"Next thing I know some gal named Naughty Dotty is in her underwear, underwater, under the Snowman, undoin' the seat from his seat. Sets him free and pulls him out of the drink. Then she starts givin' him mouth to mouth like she's Princess Charmin' and he's Cinderella's albino stepbrother just as the only judge Sam Wells, sittin' atop a lifeguard bench, says, 'I just call them as I sees them and I sees the Snowman's score a 9.3 and Soupy the winner.'

"The crowds got their cans up in a wedgie and is screamin' and callin' Sam names, even throwin' their glasses at him, some of them readin' ones; so, Sam starts ejectin' guys from the premises beginnin' with the Jocko Twins, Sam thumbin' toward the exit, sayin' 'Yer double stink; yer out of here' in an accent that's all Brooklyn. Meanwhile the Snowman and Naughty Dotty done take

135

off on a getaway scooter, her and him ridin' off into the pale sunset like in the fairy tales and he's Prince Charmin' and just learned Snow White ain't no virgin.

"Turns out the Snowman took a dive, all right, under the direction of none other than that Bert Engle feller, accordin' to TPD detective Harry The Hawk Taylor, who done placed his whole paycheck on the Snowman. The Hawk done figured out Soupy was in on the soup, too, the three of them cookin' up a big ole pot of Scambalaya. The Hawk searched Mount Knee Bow high and low, only findin' some silly lookin' mushrooms growin' in a big pile of funny smellin' shit and a couple of steel garbage can lids. Bert, he figured was the mastermind of the operation, a year or so later parlayin' his keep into a hat sellin' empire. A follow-up later by the Hawk found hisself a bunch of nunbane. Turns out numbane is none other than the common monkey ball. Just set a few in the corners of your basement. Course, them monkey balls attractin' all of them spiders will scare off more then nuns.

"Anyhow, the Snowman, Naughty Dotty and Soupy had up and gone with the circus, the two lovers gettin' hitched and performin' the opry together and Soupy doin' stunt divin' under the name the Great Minestrone.

"Anyhow, that's the last in these parts anyone has seen or heard tell of the last of the Bosizans."

I bought the good scholar another shot of enlightenment, paid and tipped Frog Prosser for the bill and hospitality. I was 26.2 sheets in the wind, not counting those in my notebook and the two bar rags. But I was determined in my quest to learn more about the legendary umpire, one Sam Wells. So, I did the crow's journey across the street to the B & J Lounge where I heard they had a fresh set of bar rags.

TALES OF CAMP CRUMB

The name is forgotten, perhaps because those who remember simply want to forget.

But the memory lingers like a child's nightmare, the repressed one deeply imbedded within the seat of the subconscious, this one deep in the forest outside Toronto, Ohio, taking one back deep into time, back to Camp Crumb, where time seems to cease and the psyche falls apart to fear.

The tale of the Hanging Tree and its vile fruit, the Hanging Head, have been passed on from generation to generation until it now looms high with urban legends. The shrinking city of Toronto, Ohio, however, is not exactly what is normally defined as urban, isolated by steep, craggy, forested hills along all sides, cut off from neighboring West Virginia and Pennsylvania by the Ohio River as if it were a medieval moat. And the trees keep secrets.

Is the tale of the Hanging Head truly a legend in the same vein as the one of the lunatic with the prosthetic hook, or just another haunted forest yarn retold over and over to scare new generations of schoolboys on pitch-dark campfire nights?

As the legend goes: a distraught man hanged himself somewhere along the cliffs of Camp Crumb sometime during the 1930s. Camp Crumb is situated a quarter-mile upstream from a dark glen waterway now known as Hanging Head Hollow, the cold-blooded stream flowing easterly below the northern face of Wallace Hill. During the latter half of the19th Century and the first decade of the 20th, Camp Crumb was a popular site for picnics and other outdoor excursions. Hundreds of initials tattooed into the bald beech tree trunks attest to this day how popular Camp Crumb once was.

These ancient trees cast dark shadows upon a terrace tasseled with ferns and sitting-sized sandstones velveted with moss—at a site

137

during midday Zenlike—a setting tranquil enough to meditate, or medicate.

But after the sun goes down.

"That's where a guy hanged himself," said Dick Walker, who has lived all his 60-plus years in this small Eastern Ohio town. "My mother and some old-timers told me how the man hanged himself with a chain at Camp Crumb and that he remained missing for two weeks until his dog dragged something gruesome home."

The evidence leading to the deceased's discovery was a limb, and not one from a beech tree.

"When the search party finally arrived at Camp Crumb," Walker said, "all they found was the man's head swinging from a chain wrapped around a limb of a beach tree near the cliffs."

His late mother told Walker the hanged man's name, but he can remember only the horrid details and that the man worked for Mike Henry at the White Front Café probably during the 1930s.

"I heard too many people talk about the Hanging Head to pass it off as some campfire tale," Walker said. "Besides, something is weird up there at night. Just makes your skin crawl. Me and five other guys tried camping out there overnight when we were young, but it was too spooky. Coming out of somewhere up the cliff above Chief Knee Bow's Cave was this whistling sound, two of them if you are listening hard enough, like blowing through the hollow eye sockets of the human skull. Needless to say, we didn't hang around very long that night.

"Plenty of other guys have tried sleeping out at Camp Crumb and that strange whistling sound chases them right back to the safety of their bar stools in town. Nobody can claim he made it to daylight."

"I remember one night like it was yesterday," said another T-towner, Pat Daugherty, about the adventure he shared with Walker. "There were six of us laughing up a storm, telling stories when we heard a chain clanging high in the beech trees somewhere above Chief Knee Bow's Cave. That whistling-moaning can come from only one type of instrument, and it's the human skull. We took off so fast we forgot to pick up our beer."

"We called it the Hanging Tree," said the late Joe Nemitt Sr., recalling boyhood excursions predating the ill-fated Walker party by two decades to the tragic site. We got scared quickly and didn't stick around."

"I wouldn't go back there with fifty guys and two kegs of beer and three crucifixes and a bucket of holy water," added Daugherty, "and I bet no one else would last more than a couple of hours. The guys and I, we won't even talk about that night."

Alex Cooper was another member of that party, notoriously named the Scaredy Cat Six, some confusion remaining whether this number refers to those who flew the coop that night or that which they were packing inside their abandoned coolers.

When told the once bucolic camp was the place for romantic interlude back in the day, Cooper replied: "I would never want to go neckin' in that neck of the woods, that's for sure. You heard of Lovers' Lane? I call that place Losers' Lane because you can lose your shirt up there, and the body that comes with it."

After that frightful night, Cooper spent months cooped up indoors before he would venture out into another mainstream bar again, and he was residing on top of one, the Spit Cup. Even after that, Cooper wouldn't stray a spittin' distance outside the premises for a river rat's age.

Exactly where this desperate deed occurred is a matter of speculation these days, says J.L. Minor, a former detective for the legendary deep-south paranormal hotspot Gizzard County, where he specialized in investing paranormal and cryptozoological activity. Minor claims to have unchained evidence that the name of the camp itself is a clue to its origin, dating back to the late 1800s.

"It was a popular place for picnics and for young lovers to take strolls back in the day when it was named Camp Crum. But something strange happened there, something inexplicable—people just stopped going there and over the years the dense forest growth overtook it. A few years back I found out there was a hanging predating the 1930s case, same exact evil occurring. Seems the founders of the once favored outdoor recreational area renamed Crum to Crumb because the foul night atmosphere causes a body to crumble like rotting fruit."

After intensive investigation, Minor stated that a curse invoked by Chief Knee Bow might have brought the evil befalling the Toronto forests, clear back when settlers first arrived, citing several disasters occurring near the south end of town, most recently in 2022 a garbage train derailment below Mount Nebo (sic), dumping a fetid payload of 40 boxcars into the Ohio River.

Minor is also investigating recent sightings of the Locust Man, a winged version of Big Foot indigenous to only the T-town area.

In his younger days, the good old boys called him Swamper. Since his swamp-boy days, Minor has been a major contributor to scientific journals devoted to the study of such obscure fauna as the skunk ape, grass man and radioactive river rats, his most recent published work documenting the correlation of alcohol consumption with pink elephant sightings.

Should the evil from Camp Crumb ever become exorcised, Minor would like to become its park ranger as he is well qualified. He had earned his prestigious Gizzard County position in a closely contested runoff with three other well qualified candidates, decided by a game of Clue in which Minor correctly guessed Colonel Mustard, in the Conservatory, with the lead pipe.

Minor says that there are plenty of other attractions besides the Hanging Tree to make hiking to an exorcised Camp Crum worthwhile such as Chief Knee Bow's Cave, and the Volkswagen van-sized monoliths Scaffold Rock, Meditation Rock and Medication Rock, the latter often confused with the former. He said that plans for constructing a Release the Belgium Hall of Fame are in the initial stages as is an annual Release the Belgium championship tentatively called *The Golden Toboggan,* and if those events go well, the modernized campgrounds parking lot could possibly hold a car show or two featuring bumpers used in the lost art of T-town bumper skiing.

Minor added there's also what may be recognized as the largest copse of nunbane growing within the heart of the forest. Said the long time paranormal investigator, "Nuns haven't been sighted there since Camp Crumb was called Camp Crum."

Said Dick Walker upon hearing that a renamed Camp Crum may open to the public someday. "I wouldn't return there on a triple-dog dare and with three cases of Dogfishhead IPA. I don't care if you are wearing a pair of lucky underwear passed down from four generations of your ancestors, you would soil them as sure as shit and be so scared you wouldn't know Medication Rock form Meditation Rock. One thing me and my buddies that night will never say again, not even in a joke, 'That's the way the cookie crumbles.' If I ever eat another cookie again, you can be sure it's made entirely out of gluten."

Made in the USA
Monee, IL
02 July 2023